LOWELL LIBSON LTD
BRITISH ART

MAASTRICHT
TEFAF: THE EUROPEAN FINE ART FAIR
10–19 March 2017

LONDON
LONDON ART WEEK
30 June–7 July 2017

NEW YORK
TEFAF: NEW YORK FALL
27–31 October 2017

LOWELL
LIBSON LTD

2017

LOWELL LIBSON LTD

BRITISH ART

3 CLIFFORD STREET · LONDON W1S 2LF

The gallery is open by appointment, Monday to Friday
The entrance is in Old Burlington Street

Telephone: +44 (0)20 7734 8686
Email: pictures@lowell-libson.com
Website: www.lowell-libson.com

Lowell Libson   *lowell@lowell-libson.com*

Jonny Yarker   *jonny@lowell-libson.com*

Cressida St Aubyn   *cressida@lowell-libson.com*

Deborah Greenhalgh   *deborah@lowell-libson.com*

We have been fortunate over the last year to have made some very significant acquisitions including a number newly discovered or, I should more accurately say, rediscovered and correctly identified works. The most remarkable of these is the previously unknown group of eleven sheets of studies by Sir Peter Lely that have been admirably researched and catalogued by my co-director, Jonny Yarker. We are delighted that this extremely important group have joined the collections at the Yale Center for British Art where they will provide a fulcrum for the further advancement of our understanding of the development and practice of British portraiture in the seventeenth century.

The newly identified self-portrait by John Hamilton Mortimer is a compelling early work by an artist who becomes increasingly fascinating as one considers his pivotal but quirky position in the artistic life of London in the second half of the eighteenth century.

Portraiture and subject painting is further represented by a superb pastel by John Russell, which depicts the famous artist's model George White as St Peter. A very fine pastel by Hoare of Bath exemplifies his mastery of this medium, whilst the remarkable Skirving of 1803 is not only the artist's masterpiece but possibly the greatest of British pastel portraits. The wonderful three-quarter length portrait by Gainsborough of Admiral Graves not only depicts a significant figure in American and British history but also represents Gainsborough's commanding control of both sitter and the technique during his final years.

We are always delighted to demonstrate our particular interests in the relationship between British and European art during the eighteenth century and in this year's selection we are especially pleased with groups of pictures that further represent our fascination with artistic training and workshop practice.

The landscape tradition runs from Alexander Cozens, by way of a perfect Cotman watercolour, a newly discovered Samuel Palmer, a trio of remarkable Ruskins to a surreal sheet of 1933 by Henry Moore.

This year we have a full programme which includes travel in the USA, fairs at TEFAF Maastricht in March and TEFAF New York in October and a drawings exhibition at our gallery in the summer for *London Art Week* of which I have recently taken on the chairmanship. We are looking forward to a very exciting year.

None of this would be possible without my very talented and dedicated colleagues: Jonny Yarker has been responsible a number of our discoveries as well for the research and writing of this catalogue whilst Deborah Greenhalgh and Cressida St Aubyn have continued to keep the show on the road. In turn, we all thank our many friends for the great personal and professional support they have given us over the last year.

LOWELL LIBSON

SIR PETER LELY 1618–1680

An important group of drawings by Sir Peter Lely

A group of thirteen sheets of drawings of hands: comprising eleven autograph drawings by Lely and two drawings by members of Lely's workshop.
Mostly red, white and black chalks on buff wrapping paper
Various sizes between 100 × 92 mm and 380 × 295 mm
Drawn at various times c.1650s and 1660s

COLLECTIONS
Possibly, Richard Gibson (d.1690), a gift from the artist;
Possibly, Michael Rosse, son-in-law of the above, to 1723;
Private collection, UK, acquired in the 1960s, to 2016;
Acquired by Lowell Libson Ltd, May 2016;
Yale Center for British Art, New Haven, acquired from the above, 2016.

left: Sir Peter Lely *Lady Anna Grey, c.*1658
Oil on canvas · 50 × 40 inches · 1270 × 1015 mm
Private collection.

Mr Lilly did often say to Mr. F[ever] that painting was nothing else but draft.[1]

This remarkable, previously unknown group of eleven sheets constitute a highly significant addition to Lely's oeuvre and help elucidate important aspects of his working practice. The drawings are all of exquisitely rendered hands and arms, executed rapidly in black and white chalk on buff coloured paper. These beautifully articulated studies were all made from models and as a result offer a remarkable working archive of life studies which Lely used in his finished portraits. Drawings by Lely are rare – only approximately 80 sheets survive – the contemporary evidence confirms that at Lely's death there were a great many more, now lost or unrecorded.[2] The discovery of this group of drawings is therefore highly significant; the only comparable surviving group are the thirty drawings Lely made of the Garter procession in 1667, which are now scattered across the world.[3] Whilst the Garter sheets are highly finished studies, the present set of drawings are more spontaneous and represent the most important body of *ad vivum* drawings by Lely in existence. The collection arguably offers more insight into Lely's processes and practice as a painter providing a fresh perspective on the development of British portraiture between Van Dyck and Joshua Reynolds.

opposite: detail from Drawing B

Peter Lely as draughtsman
Little is known of the drawings of Lely's earliest master in Haarlem, Frans Pieter de Grebber, as Lindsay Stainton has pointed out, Lely's own early drawings show the influence of Cornelius van Poelenburgh.[4] A pair of drawings in the British Museum, *Arcadian scene with a nymph advancing towards a couple seated* and *The Finding of Moses* both of *c.*1641, show the early influence of van Poelenburgh.[5] A few landscape studies, together with a couple of presentation drawings for early subject pictures have also survived, but the majority of Lely's known drawings are preparatory studies for portraits. A number of highly finished chalk portraits survive. These compelling studies include the tender depiction of his friend *Sir Charles Cotterell,* now in the British Museum and the famed self-portrait, described by contemporaries as 'craions' they were clearly designed as finished works of art and are the only drawings he signed.[6] Indeed a group were included in Lely's posthumous sale where his executor, Roger North, specifically listed them as being 'in Ebony frames' and therefore ready for display.[7] But these finished works are unusual, the majority of Lely's surviving drawings relate directly to his work as a portrait painter.

We know quite a lot about Lely's studio practice, thanks to a number of contemporary accounts and it is clear that drawing was central to his production of painted portraits. Lely seems to have made quick chalk sketches to catch a sitter's likeness at a first sitting. In 1673 the painter William Gandy made observations about Lely's methods, noting that he first: 'slightly chalks out the body', then laid in the face, and, 'the person sitting in his intended posture', he next sketched in the hands and clothes adding: 'He does all this by the life presently whilst the person stays so you have a picture in an instant.'[8] This process is confirmed by another account from a contemporary. In the 1670s Lely's friends, the painter Mary Beale and her husband Charles, a patent clerk, art dealer and colourman, commissioned a number of portraits from him, including one of the future Archbishop of Canterbury, John Tillotson. During the initial sitting with Tillotson, Beale observed Lely make a drawing: 'first in chalk rudely & afterwards in colours and rubbed upon that a little colour very thin in places for the shadows, and laid a touch of light upon the heightening of the forehead.'[9] This 'rude' study was evidently designed to serve as a guide to Lely himself, at the same time acting as important material for use in his busy and productive studio.

These very rapid, full-compositional studies are exceptionally rare and it is possible that Gandy and Beale were describing an ideal method rather than Lely's normal practice. It seems more likely that Lely relied on stock poses and instead made refinements from the life in the form of studies of hands, arms and costume.

The evidence suggests that Lely used drawings at every stage of the portraiture process. He probably showed prospective sitters drawings with various poses worked out to help them choose how they wished to be depicted; he made compositional sketches, such as that of Tillotson described by Beale, and then made studies as the painting progressed to work out costumes, poses and gestures. It is the latter group of studies which survive in greater numbers, suggesting that they were far more central to Lely's practice. Beale describes Lely making a drawing whilst he was painting a portrait Beale had commissioned of his son, also called Charles, in 1672. Beale noted that after: 'Mr Lely dead coloured my son

Charles picture… he took a drawing upon paper after an Indian gown which he had put on his back, in order to the finishing of the Drapery of it.'[10] The evidence points to Lely having produced hand and arm studies in the same manner whilst he worked on a portrait. These sheets had a practical purpose. Hands and draperies constituted areas of secondary importance in the finished portrait, Lely would have reserved the valuable time he had with the sitter to concentrate on the face and expression. The drawings he therefore made during a sitting could be worked up on the canvas by assistants, or at the very least in the absence of the sitter.

Scholars have been slow to appreciate these process drawings, made during the execution of a portrait. Lely was famed for having stock poses, in his accounts, Lely's executor, Roger North, added a number to Lely's unfinished portraits, suggesting that each number corresponded to an established pose: 'Whole length postures No. 8 & 1', and 'Sr. Ralph Verney ½ 49', for example.[11] Lely's reliance on formulaic poses, on studio assistance and on replicating his own compositions has resulted in a degree of critical neglect. As Oliver Miller observed: 'Lely's reputation has suffered because it has made to rest so often on portraits in which he himself had no part and because among the portraits he did paint there is not sufficient variety in scale, in layout or in the relationship between the sitter and the spectator.'[12] But the versatility and subtlety of Lely's portraiture is instantly visible in the hand studies he made during sittings. These intimate sheets neatly communicate Lely's virtuosity and creativity, attempting to inject life into his conventionally arranged subject. A famous sheet in the Ashmolean of three hands – long identified as relating to two portraits, *Frances Stuart, later Duchess of Richmond* and *Diana Kirke, later Countess of Oxford* – shows how he experimented with

opposite: Drawing A
Black, white and red chalk on buff paper
14 × 11 inches · 355 × 280 mm

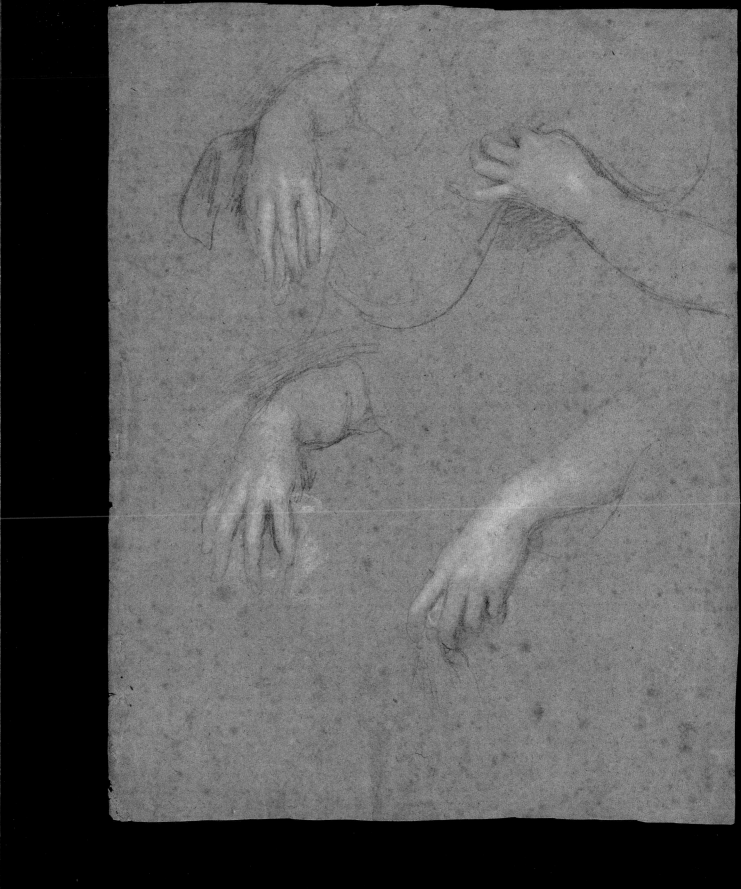

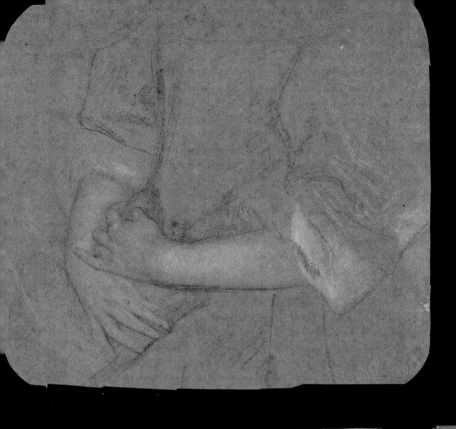

left: Drawing B
Black, white and red chalk on buff paper
8⅞ × 10½ inches · 225 × 267 mm

below left: Drawing C
Black, white and red chalk on buff paper
13½ × 10½ inches · 344 × 268 mm

below: Drawing D
Black, white and red chalk on buff paper
15 × 11⅝ inches · 380 × 295 mm

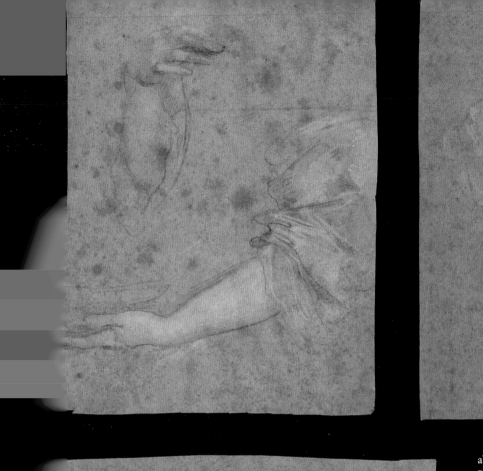

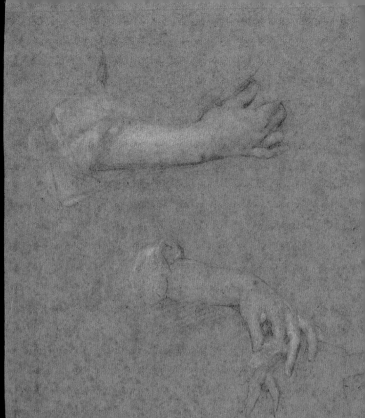

above left: Drawing E
Black, white and red chalk on buff paper
13¾ × 10⅜ inches · 350 × 265 mm

above: Drawing F
Black, white and red chalk on buff paper
11 × 9¾ inches · 280 × 250 mm

left: Drawing G
Black, white and red chalk on buff paper
11½ × 9¼ inches · 293 × 235 mm

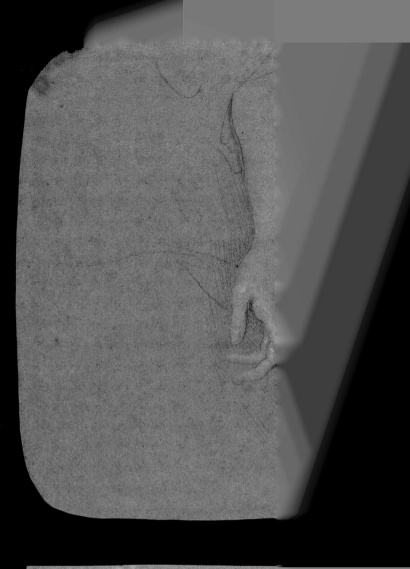

Drawing I
and red chalk on buff paper
ches · 323 × 260 mm

: Drawing H
and red chalk on buff paper
hes · 267 × 210 mm

ving J
and red chalk on buff paper
hes · 137 × 160 mm

rawing K
and red chalk on buff paper
s · 100 × 92mm

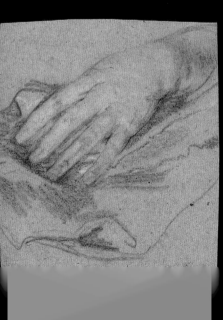

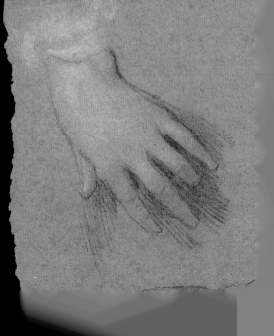

the careful articulation of fingers and the iconography of his sitters.[13] It is precisely this deliberate and exquisite versatility which is evident in the rediscovered group of thirteen hand studies discussed below.

The re-discovered drawings

The eleven sheets which comprise this spectacular, rediscovered group of drawings were all made from the life by Lely to help establish poses in his portraiture. The drawings are mostly on a characteristic buff-coloured paper, identical to that used in the Fitzwilliam, Ashmolean and Courtauld hand studies. All the drawings are executed in a distinctive combination of black and white chalks, whilst nine of the studies are strengthened with red or flesh coloured chalks. Lely was famous amongst his contemporaries for his use of media, particularly coloured chalks. Christiaan Huygens, who visited Lely's studio in 1663, gave a detailed account of his techniques and materials in the letters he sent to his brother, Constantin. On his first visit Huygens noted

Lely used a paper that was 'un peu griastre' (somewhat greyish, or merely coloured), 'et n'employe de couleurs que dans le visage et cela encore légerement.'[14]

The drawings can be separated into two distinct groups. Nine of the sheets show compositional studies of arms and hands, carefully and beautifully rendered; evidently made in preparation for portraits. The remaining four sheets are single studies of hands, handled more rapidly and schematically. All the drawings seem first to have been worked in black chalk, then strengthened with white or coloured chalk. This method fits contemporary descriptions of Lely's practice. Gandy recorded an occasion when Lely demonstrated his method of drawing a figure:

Mr Lilly draws all things in this manner… as suppose it is a Figure. As bodys Armes legs he draws it in angles though there be never so many muscles, only a right stroke in this manner but is pretty sure in drawing of these angles, these are as foundations, then he mends it by degrees, till you see some muscles appear.[15]

below left: Drawing M
Circle of Peter Lely
Black and white chalk on buff paper
10⅜ × 9½ inches · 263 × 240mm

below right: Drawing L
Circle of Peter Lely
Black and white chalk on buff paper
8¼ × 10¾ inches · 210 × 275mm

This approach is legible in *Drawing I*, the two hand studies have been constructed with a rapid black chalk line, the shadow has been added in 'angles', or hatching, to strengthen or 'mend' the arms profile. This has been amplified by the addition of highlights in white and red chalk.

Turning to the subject matter of the drawings, some clearly relate closely to completed portraits. *Drawing B* is a detailed, carefully articulated study for the hands of *Lady Anna Grey*, a portrait completed in 1658. The drawing is unusual in being such a precise design for the finished image, suggesting that Lely made the drawing during a sitting and passed it to an assistant for use in completing the finished portrait. *Drawing M.* is equally literal, the meticulously hatched hand study shows a hand holding a sprig of orange blossom was deployed by Lely in at least two portraits: *Elizabeth, Countess of Kildare* painted in c.1679 and now in the Tate Gallery, London and *Lady Elizabeth Tollemache, later Duchess of Argyll*.

Several of the sheets show Lely exploring variations on familiar compositions. *Drawing E.* is a careful design for a seated female figure, her left hand raised to her chest, the left hand resting in her lap. This is a variant on a prototype pose which Lely deployed in numerous portraits – for example the portrait of *Mary Bagot, Countess of Middlesex and Dorset* and *Lady Penelope Nicholas* painted in 1662 – but it seems not to link to a specific, known painting. This is true of a number of the studies, *Drawing D* for example, clearly fits the general arrangement of one of Lely's stock poses, in this case, a woman seated with her left hand placed on her chest and her right hand leaning on a rock, the purpose of *Drawing D* was clearly to offer a specific alternative on a general theme, whilst working on a portrait. The meticulous rendering of the hands, particularly the articulation of the fingers demonstrates Lely's remarkable ability to vary a familiar

format, it also points to the importance of these drawings within the creative process. The most intensely rendered of the sheets, *Drawing A*, *Drawing C*, and *Drawing F*, for example, show both the facility of Lely's handling and the breadth of his imagination. Throughout the drawings Lely shows hands in various expressive positions, carefully holding drapery and the fingers arranged differently in each: resting on a basin, holding an orb, flowers, hands gesturing and hands relaxed. It is the variations which point to these drawings having been made directly from the life, in the manner that Charles Beale described Lely drawing a section of 'Indian gown' above.

Initial investigation suggests that the drawings date from across his career. The dating of *Lady Anna Grey* to the 1650s suggests that some of the sheets were made before the Restoration, but the majority seem likely to date from the 1660s when Lely was at the height of his power and his studio was most productive. Further research will undoubtedly tie more of the drawings to specific paintings.

History of the drawings

The evidence of Lely's surviving drawings suggests that a large number were left in his studio at his death. Studies, such as the sheet of arms and hands in the Ashmolean Museum, are marked with the distinctive 'PL' stamp, a mark applied to drawings found in Lely's studio after his death by his executor, Roger North.[16] Other drawings which must have been in the studio are not marked, such as the great *Self-Portrait*, either because they were not offered for sale or because they left the studio before the sale. The recently discovered group of drawings are not marked and seem likely to have left the studio before Lely's death.

The internal evidence of the drawings themselves does not offer much help. The drawings appear to have been mounted

Sir Peter Lely
Sir Charles Cotterell, c.1660
Black, red and white chalk on brown-grey paper
10⅞ × 7⅝ inches · 277 × 194 mm
Signed with monogram: 'PL fe'
© The Trustees of the British Museum

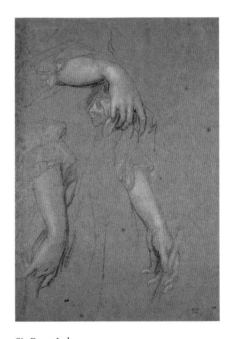

Sir Peter Lely
Studies of Hands
Chalk on buff paper · 15 × 10½ inches · 382 × 268 mm
© Ashmolean Museum, University of Oxford

into an album at the end of the seventeenth century or very early in the eighteenth century and the paper of the album has been dated by Peter Bower to *c*.1700. A fascicle of sheets containing this group of drawings were detached from a larger album at some stage and the backing sheet for *Drawing A* which originally formed the start of this section of the album is carefully inscribed, in an eighteenth-century hand: 'Drawings by Sir Peter Lely (undoubted)'. *Drawing C* is inscribed on the verso '*By Sir Peter Lely*' in an early eighteenth-century hand. There are no other collectors marks in evidence, so we know that the drawings did not form part of the substantial group of Lely drawings that belonged to the painter Jonathan Richardson.[17] Many of Richardson's drawings were acquired by his son-in-law, the painter, Thomas Hudson, this included a number of sheets by Lely, including the two now in the Witt Collection at the Courtauld.

One possible provenance is that they were given by Lely to his friend and fellow-painter Richard Gibson. We know Gibson owned a substantial number of drawings by Lely. Gibson left them to his son-in-law, Michael Rosse, a jeweller, and they appear in his posthumous sale in April 1723. The *Catalogue of the Collection of Mr Michael Rosse*, contains ten lots described as: '10 Hands, &c. Sir *Peter Lely*.'[18] No priced copy of the Rosse catalogue survives making it impossible to reconstruct the subsequent history of his collection.

This group of drawings appear to have been detached from perhaps a larger collection of drawings in an album as indicated by the inscribed section heading. This section appears to have remained intact and was

acquired by a British collector in the 1960s. This group has remained in total obscurity until its recent appearance on the market.

Conclusion

This is perhaps the most important group of drawings by Peter Lely to come on the market since the eighteenth century. It is certainly the largest intact single group of compositional studies by Lely known to survive. The beautifully rendered studies were all made from models and as a result offer a remarkable working archive of life studies which Lely used in his finished portraits. The group, when considered together, offers an unprecedented insight into Lely's working method. More broadly, the studies offer vital evidence for the role of drawing in the evolution of British portraiture in the generation after Van Dyck.

These drawings will be included by Catharine MacLeod and Diana Dethloff in their forthcoming catalogue raisonné of the paintings and drawings of Sir Peter Lely.

NOTES

1 London, British Library, Add. MS 22950.f.18r.
2 Diana Dethloff, 'Lely, Drawing, and the Training of Artists', in eds. Mark Hallett, Nigel Llewellyn, and Martin Myrone, *Court, Country, City British Art and Architecture 1660–1735*, New Haven and London, 2016, p.297.
3 16 of the drawings are in the collection of the British Museum, the only other significant group of Lely drawings to remain in-tact. Other sheets are widely dispersed. See Oliver Millar, *Sir Peter Lely*, exh.cat., London (National Portrait Gallery), 1978, pp.80–87.
4 Eds. Lindsay Stainton and Christopher White, *Drawing in England, from Hilliard to Hogarth*, exh.cat., London (British Museum), 1987, p.30.

5 Ed. Caroline Campbell, *Peter Lely a Lyrical Vision*, exh.cat., London (Courtauld Gallery), 2013, p.49.
6 Eds. Lindsay Stainton and Christopher White, *Drawing in England, from Hilliard to Hogarth*, exh.cat., London (British Museum), 1987, p.31.
7 See Diana Dethloff, 'The Executors' Account Book and the Dispersal of Sir Peter Lely's Collection', *The Journal of the History of Collections*, 8, no.1, 1996, p.29.
8 London, British Library, Add. MS 22950.f.3.
9 G. Vertue, eds. L. Cust and A. Hind, 'The Notebooks of George Vertue', *The Walpole Society*, London, 1929–47, IV, p.172.
10 G. Vertue, eds. L. Cust and A. Hind, 'The Notebooks of George Vertue', *The Walpole Society*, London, 1929–47, IV, p.172.
11 Eds. Catharine MacLeod and Julia Alexander, *Painted Ladies: Women at the Court of Charles II*, exh.cat., London (National Portrait Gallery), 2001, p.55.
12 Oliver Millar, *Sir Peter Lely*, exh.cat., London (National Portrait Gallery), 1978, p.27.
13 For the Ashmolean sheet see Eds. Catharine MacLeod and Julia Alexander, *Painted Ladies: Women at the Court of Charles II*, exh.cat., London (National Portrait Gallery), 2001, p.57.
14 Quoted in Eds. Lindsay Stainton and Christopher White, *Drawing in England, from Hilliard to Hogarth*, exh.cat., London (British Museum), 1987, p.31.
15 Quoted in Diana Dethloff, 'Lely, Drawing, and the Training of Artists', in eds. Mark Hallett, Nigel Llewellyn, and Martin Myrone, *Court, Country, City British Art and Architecture 1660–1735*, New Haven and London, 2016, p.296.
16 Diana Dethloff, 'The Executors' Account Book and the Dispersal of Sir Peter Lely's Collection', *The Journal of the History of Collections*, 8, no.1, 1996, p.16.
17 The Richardson sale in 1747 (11th night lot 10) contained a book of Lely's drawings and there were quite a few in the junior Richardson sale (day 3, lots 24 and 68, day 4 lot 21, day 7 lot 12).
18 *A Catalogue of the Collection of Mr Michael Rosse…*, 24th, 25th and 26th April, 1723, lot 18, 20, 22, 25, 57, 60, 82, 86, 89 (12 Hands, &c. Sir *Peter Lely*).

WILLIAM HOARE OF BATH RA 1707–1792

William Folkes of Hillington Hall, Norfolk

Pastel
24 × 18 inches · 610 × 458 mm
Drawn in c.1740
In the original architrave frame probably
from the workshop of Isaac Gosset

COLLECTIONS
William Folkes (1700–1773);
Sir Martin Browne ffolkes, 1st Bt. (1749–1821)
son of the above;
Sir William Browne ffolkes, 2nd Bt.
(1786–1860;
Sir William Browne ffolkes, 3rd Bt,
(1847–1912) grandson of the above;
Dorothy Dawnay, Hillington Hall, Norfolk,
(1876–1957), daughter of the above;
George William ffolkes Dawnay,
son of the above, to 1976;
Dawnay sale, Sotheby's London,
18th December 1976, lot 199;
Private collection, to 2016.

LITERATURE
Neil Jeffares, *A Dictionary of Pastellists
before 1800*, online edition, J.395.119.

This powerful portrait depicts the lawyer William Folkes, the younger son of Martin Folkes and his wife, Dorothy, second daughter of Sir William Hovell of Hillington Hall, near King's Lynn in Norfolk. Folkes's elder brother was the celebrated antiquary, numismatist, mathematician and eventually President of the Royal Society, Martin Folkes. Drawn by William Hoare of Bath in about 1740, the portrait of Folkes neatly demonstrates the fashion for pastels in the mid-eighteenth century and the exceptional level they achieved.

Many material and practical factors contributed to the popularity of pastels during the eighteenth century: the distinctive light and brilliant surface, the strength of colours, the simplicity of tools required to make them, the relative speed with which they could be completed as well as their essentially domestic scale and informal character. These inherent strengths, were amplified by a burgeoning market for portraiture at all levels in Britain during the century and the advancement of certain technologies, which made pastel a highly popular medium in which to work. As George Vertue noted, pastels were 'much easier in the execution than Oil colours', because they were quicker to execute and required no drying time. These qualities allowed pastel painters greater flexibility than practitioners in oil, enabling pastellists to be itinerant and set up in fashionable spa towns, such as Bath, where Hoare established himself in 1738.

Artists and patrons appreciated the distinctive optical properties of painting in pastel: the exquisite luminosity, bright unchanging colours and unmistakable bloom, or fleur, that enlivens the complexion of the sitter. For artists, pastels also offered

an efficient use of time. William Hoare was one of the popularisers of the medium in Britain. Hoare had been trained in London with Giuseppe Grisoni, who in 1728 took him to Italy. In Rome and perhaps in Venice, he would have been able to study drawings in coloured crayons and he may have met important practitioners such as Bernardo Luti and Rosalba Carriera.[1] Vertue specifically noted the success of pastellists 'that had been to Italy to study', registering the decorative quality of their works: 'looking pleasant… coverd with a glass large Gold Frames was much commended. for novelty.'[2] Francis Cotes, who wrote a treatise on his art which was published posthumously in the *European Magazine*, observed: 'Crayon pictures, when finely painted, are superlatively beautiful, and decorative in a very high degree in apartments that are not too large; for having their surface dry, they partake in appearance of the effect of Fresco, and by candle light are luminous and beautiful beyond all other pictures.'[3]

William Hoare was much in demand by fashionable sitters. William Folkes was almost certainly introduced to Hoare by his brother, Martin Folkes. Martin Folkes had been painted by Hoare and was an intimate of the artistic circles in London in which Hoare moved.[4] Folkes was the subject of a famous portrait by William Hogarth, which he left to the Royal Society, a bust by Louis-François Roubiliac, now at Petworth and countless other portraits and commemorative medals.[5] The relationship with Roubiliac is significant, as William Folkes was responsible for commissioning the monument to the parents of his first wife Cecilia, Jane and Thomas Kerridge at

Framlingham in Suffolk in 1744.[6] Martin and William Folkes were close; Martin helped William to the appointment of agent to John, 2nd Duke of Montagu and attempted to find him a parliamentary seat. William Folkes married, as his second wife, the only daughter and heiress of Sir William Browne, President of the Royal College of Physicians a long-standing friend and correspondent of Martin.

Hoare's portrait of William demonstrates his qualities as a pastellist; the striking characterisation and plasticity of the sitter's features, contrasts with the simple costume. Hoare seems to have left William Folkes's left arm only partially blocked-in, creating the sense of shadow and recession by leaving the passage as under drawing. Hoare's portrait of William Folkes perfectly fits contemporary descriptions of the decorative qualities of the medium, housed, as it is, in a contemporary carved gilt-frame. The

architectural style, with its squared corners, is identical to the type of frame described by Arthur Pond as an 'architrave gold frame' and associated with the neo-Palladian interiors of William Kent and Isaac Ware.[7] William Hoare, like Pond, employed the carver and gilder Isaac Gosset to produce his pastel frames. In 1763 Hoare specifically described Gosset as 'my framemaker' when receiving payment from Lady Egremont.

Dorothy Richardson visited Hoare's studio in Bath during the 1760s where she noted:

'I believe he is the best Crayon Painter in the Kingdom, & I can form no higher Idea of that Art, either as to Delicacy Colouring or expression than what I saw in his Pictures, which if they do not reach perfection, I am sure are very near it.'[8] A powerful, expressive pastel, Hoare's depiction of William Folkes is preserved in exceptional condition and perfectly encapsulates why Hoare was so highly regarded.

NOTES

1   Evelyn Newby suggested that Hoare's use of pastel responded to both Luti and Rosalba see Evelyn Newby, *William Hoare of Bath*, exh.cat., Bath (Victoria Art Gallery), 1990, p.10.
2   G. Vertue, eds. L. Cust and A. Hind, 'The Notebooks of George Vertue', *The Walpole Society*, London, 1929–47, III, p.109.
3   Francis Cotes, *The European Magazine, and London Review*, February 1797, p.84.
4   Evelyn Newby suggested that Hoare's use of pastel responded to both Luti and Rosalba see Evelyn Newby, *William Hoare of Bath*, exh.cat., Bath (Victoria Art Gallery), 1990, p.10.
5   For an iconography of Martin Folkes see John Kerslake, *Early Georgian Portraits*, London, 1977, I, pp.76–78.
6   D. Bindman and M. Baker, *Roubiliac and the Eighteenth-century Monument: Sculpture as Theatre*, New Haven and London, 1995, p.375, n.12 and cat.22.
7   Jacob Simon, *The Art of the Picture Frame: Artists, Patrons and the Framing of Portraits in Britain*, 1997, p.62.
8   Hugh Belsey, 'A Visit to the Studios of Gainsborough and Hoare', *The Burlington Magazine*, 192, no.1007, February 1987, p.109.

William Hoare of Bath
Colonel John and Sarah Lee
Pastel over pencil on paper laid on canvas
Each 23½ × 17¾ inches · 595 × 450 mm
Executed in the late 1740s
National Gallery of Art, Washington DC
(formerly with Lowell Libson Ltd)

JOHN HAMILTON MORTIMER 1740–1779

Self-portrait

Oil on canvas
30 × 25⅛ inches · 762 × 638 mm
verso: after Sir Joshua Reynolds,
a self-portrait
Painted *c.*1758

COLLECTIONS
(Probably) Edward Sacheverell Pole,
Radburne Hall Derbyshire;
Henry Chandos-Pole-Gell (1829–1902),
Radburne Hall, Derby, who also inherited
Hopton Hall by reversion in 1863 under the
terms of the will of Philip Gell (1775–1842);
Lt. Col. John Chandos-Pole (1909–1993),
Newnham Hall, Daventry, grandson of the
above;
By descent to 2015.

LITERATURE
Algernon Graves and Walter V. Cronin,
*A History of the works of Sir Joshua Reynolds
PRA*, London, 1901, IV, p.1394;
David Manning, *Sir Joshua Reynolds:
A Complete Catalogue of his Paintings*, New
Haven and London, 2000, p.48, no.13c.

Joseph Wright of Derby *Study of a boy*
[here identified as John Hamilton Mortimer]
Pencil · 7½ × 5½ inches · 190 × 139 mm
Private collection, UK

This sensitively handled oil is the earliest
recorded self-portrait by John Hamilton
Mortimer, executed circa 1758, shortly
after Mortimer had entered the studio of
Thomas Hudson. It was in Hudson's studio
that Mortimer met Joseph Wright of Derby,
with whom he had a life-long friendship and
working relationship. Previously unpublished, this painting sheds significant light
on Mortimer's working practices and on the
activities of young artists in the 1750s, the
decade before the foundation of the Royal
Academy. Its rediscovery also underlines
what a compelling and intelligent painter
Mortimer was, raising significant questions
about his relationship with Wright of Derby.
The work is also unfinished offering valuable
insights into the working methods of British
painters at a transitional moment in the
emergence of an indigenous school of art.

John Hamilton Mortimer was born in
Eastbourne, Sussex the fifth and youngest
child of Thomas Mortimer, a mill owner
and customs officer. The landscape painter
and diarist, Joseph Farington recorded
that Mortimer: 'he began to draw when
very young.'[1] In 1756 or 1757 Mortimer's
father paid £100 for him to work in the
studio of Thomas Hudson. By the 1750s
an artistic system had emerged in Britain
which meant drawing from the antique and
life model were largely taught in a series
of private organisations – including the
St Martin's Lane Academy and Shipley's
drawing academy – whilst the practical
role of a painter was learnt in the atelier of
an established master. In Hudson's studio,
we know, Mortimer would have been
taught to draw, initially by copying old
master drawings or prints from Hudson's
own collection.[2] Hudson would also have
instructed Mortimer in the use of oil paint,
a fact which is significant when considering
the confident execution of the present boldly
handled work.

Mortimer's earliest biographers tell
us that he grew tired of Hudson's studio
regime and left after a year. Hudson's
most famous student, Joshua Reynolds,
similarly rebelled over the repetitive nature
of Hudson's teaching method. Mortimer
worked instead with the painter and political
radical, Robert Edge Pine.

We have a sense of Mortimer's powers
as a draughtsman at this period from a
series of highly finished drawings after
sculptures and life-drawings preserved in
the collection of the Society of Arts.[3] Two
of the life drawings are signed and dated
1758 and 1759, they were probably made at
the St Martin's Lane Academy. Mortimer
was awarded a premium by the Society of
Arts for the second drawing, the Minutes
recording 'Drawings of Human Figures
from living Models at Academy of Artists
in St. Martin's Lane, in Chalks, by Young
Men under 24 years to divide 30 Guineas…
1759 John Mortimer pupil of Mr Pine, 2nd
share.'[4] At the same time Mortimer was
drawing from casts. An article in *The Monthly
Magazine* noted:
whilst he was here [with Hudson], *and for a
considerable time afterwards, he attended the
Duke of Richmond's Gallery, which was, indeed,
his school, and where his assiduity, his exertions,
and his opening powers were so much noticed
by Cipriani, and the late Mr Moser, that they*

represented him so favourably to the illustrious nobleman… that he wished very much to have retained him in his house.[5]

Mortimer did not become the 'house' painter to Charles Lennox, 3rd Duke of Richmond, but it is notable that his 'opening powers' were recognised by contemporaries.

A series of nine black and white chalk character studies preserved in the Sir John Soane's Museum date from roughly 1758. Showing different heads observed from oblique angles, the studies show the influence of Giovanni-Battista Piazzetta and the Irish portraitist Thomas Frye, whose own head studies published as mezzotints were extremely popular. The drawings betray Mortimer's interest in certain viewpoints and physiognomic stylisations. For example, he seems to have been attracted to showing figures from below; many of the sitters are shown with distinctive flared nostrils, upturned noses and small, sharply drawn mouths, with heavily shadowed lower-lips.

These features are all apparent in Mortimer's earliest self-portrait. A remarkably confident work made at the beginning of his training, the present portrait combines several important themes which would be consistent features of his career.

The first is self-portraiture itself. Mortimer, like his older friend Joseph Wright of Derby, was fascinated by self-portraiture. Wright produced numerous images of himself over his career beginning with a romantic depiction in Van Dyck costume now in Derby Museum and Art Gallery. Possibly painted when Wright was working in Hudson's studio for the second time, it is similar in approach and handling to our self-portrait by Mortimer.[6] The sitter in our portrait is instantly recognisable as Mortimer from his later self-portraits. Four years after beginning the present study, he produced another self-portrait, which he exhibited at the Society of Artists in 1762. John Sunderland identified the work with a painting formerly in the collection of Mortimer's descendants which is now known only from a poor quality black and white photograph.[7] It is notable that his first exhibited work, at the first exhibition of living British art in London, was a self-portrait. Like Wright, Mortimer continued to produce self-portraits throughout his career. In the mid-1760s Mortimer painted a conversation piece of himself, his father, Thomas and brother Charles Smith now in the Yale Center for British Art in New Haven. Mortimer is the seated figure in the foreground of the Yale conversation piece, his features – the retroussé nose, the short, dark hair, thick bottom lip and slight dimple in the chin – are the same, but older than in our portrait.

The second is artistic education. Again, like Wright, Mortimer was clearly fascinated by the process of learning to paint and draw and like Wright he produced a series of celebrated images of artists at work. The most instructive is a famous self-portrait of himself seated at a drawing board with a student, presumably correcting the student's drawing of the casts laid on the table in front of them.[8] The painting is known in two versions, in the second, now in the Royal Academy of Arts, London, Mortimer included the sculptor Joseph Wilton, who had supervised his own time drawing in the Duke of Richmond's academy.[9] In 1769 Mortimer was appointed a director of the Maiden Lane Academy by the Society of Artists and was required to set the life model along with Ozias Humphry, Robert Edge Pine, George Stubbs, Joseph Wright and Johan Zoffany. According to the Minutes of the Society of Artists, Mortimer was

required: 'to wait upon Dr [William] Hunter and… desire the favour of him to dissect a human figure for the use of the Academy.'[10]

This newly discovered self-portrait is therefore particularly important as it combines these two ideas, showing, as it does, Mortimer at work. Although unfinished, Mortimer depicts himself holding a drawing board, presumably in the process of making a study with a porte crayon. Mortimer's upturned eyes and concentrated expression possibly suggests that he was attempting to depict himself in the process of drawing a sculpture or cast, given the date, probably at the Duke of Richmond's Sculpture Gallery. That Mortimer painted this study is also instructive. Given that in 1758 Mortimer was still apprenticed to Thomas Hudson, he would naturally be learning to handle oil. The blond ground, use of liquid brown paint to block in the costume and the careful build-up of colour, all accords with Hudson's own technique. So too does the format, Mortimer has shown

himself in a feigned oval, similar to many of Hudson's most successful portraits of the period and a format Mortimer himself adopts in his portraiture of the 1760s.

Provenance

This unfinished painting was only recently rediscovered, because Mortimer seemingly reused the canvas. The painting has traditionally said to have come from Hopton Hall in Derbyshire and of depicting Thomas Haden.[11] It is first definitely recorded at Radburne Hall in Derbyshire in the collection of Henry Chandos-Pole-Gell. Radburne Hall is notable as the location of one of Mortimer's most ambitious projects. With Joseph Wright of Derby, Mortimer was commissioned by Edward Sacheverell Pole to decorate the Saloon. Wright supplied portraits of Pole, a Colonel in the 23rd Foot of Royal Welsh Fusiliers, his wife, and also to provide four overdoor panels of candle-light subjects. Mortimer was commissioned to complete two large scenes from classical

John Hamilton Mortimer
Self-portrait with his Father and his Brother, early 1760s
Oil on canvas · 30 × 25 inches · 762 × 635 mm
Yale Center for British Art, Paul Mellon Collection

John Hamilton Mortimer
Youth looking up, c.1758–60
Black chalk with white heightening on toned paper
13⅜ × 10 inches · 340 × 255 mm
Courtesy of the Trustees of Sir John Soane's Museum

John Hamilton Mortimer
Woman resting her cheek on her left hand, c.1758–60
Black chalk with white heightening on toned paper
15 × 13⅜ inches · 380 × 340 mm
Courtesy of the Trustees of Sir John Soane's Museum

antiquity in the grand manner, representing the *Blind Belisarius* and *Caius Marius on the Ruins of Carthage*, as well as an Allegory of the Arts as a fifth overdoor. Mortimer was paid 100 guineas each for the *Belisarius* and the *Caius Marius* and 50 guineas for the overdoor.

The identification of the portrait as Thomas Haden, rather than Mortimer, rested on its similarity to a drawing apparently showing the same sitter by Joseph Wright of Derby. The drawing, also at Radburne Hall, shows a young boy, with similar features to Mortimer – retroussé nose, full-lips, and slight dimple in the chin

– but the pose is slightly different, Wright has shown the sitter leaning on his left hand. It was the pose which led to Nicholson identifying the drawing as a study for Wright's painting of *Edwin (from Dr Beattie's Minstrel)* and therefore Thomas Haden.[12] But the boy in the drawing at Radburne hall bears no resemblance to the finished painting of *Edwin*. The drawing is therefore likely to show not Haden, but Mortimer. This idea is given strength by the fact that the portrait drawing has long been mounted with a drawing by Mortimer.[13] The Mortimer shows a study after Moreelse's *Lady as Shepherdess* and is dated to Sunderland

Robert Blyth, after John Hamilton Mortimer
Self-portrait, 1782
Etching · 15¼ × 12⅛ inches · 387 × 307 mm
© The Trustees of the British Museum

Valentine Green, after John Hamilton Mortimer
Portrait after a self-portrait, 1779
Mezzotint · 17⅝ × 12⅞ inches · 453 × 326 mm
© The Trustees of the British Museum

to 1775–1778.[14] The figure is copied from a painting that was in the collection of Mortimer's great friend and patron, Dr Benjamin Bates. The Mortimer drawing was therefore executed whilst he was working at Radburne and seems likely to have been acquired by Edward Sacheverell Pole.

This does raise the question of why two portrait studies of Mortimer, apparently made twenty years earlier, stayed at Radburne. In the case of our self-portrait, it is clear Mortimer was reusing an old canvas. Mortimer painted on the verso a copy of Joshua Reynolds's 1774 self-portrait.[15] The reason for Mortimer's copy is unclear. Mortimer admired Reynolds greatly, he dedicated a series of fifteen etchings to Reynolds in 1778 and was highly conscious of *The Discourses*. Indeed, when he exhibited the Radburne *Belisarius* at the Society of Artists in 1772, Mortimer noted in the *Candid Observations* which he penned anonymously with Thomas Jones: 'It appears evident here, the Painter has carefully read Sir Joshua Reynolds's last lecture, and has perhaps too closely adhered to the Principles of the Bolognian School.'[16]

Precisely why Mortimer painted a copy of Reynolds's self-portrait is unclear, but it is almost certainly the route of the muddle over provenance. Philip Gell, whose property descended through his only daughter, Isabella, to the Chandos-Pole family of Radburne Hall, was painted by Reynolds.[17] Gell's full-length portrait by Reynolds is preserved at Radburne and Reynolds's sitters' books record several appointments with Gell between 1768 and 1772 perhaps fuelling the idea that Mortimer's self-portrait had once been at Hopton. But without any definitive evidence to the contrary, it seems far more likely that the painting was acquired by Edward Sacheverell Pole. More recently the present painting passed, with other Gell pictures from Hopton, to Colonel John Chandos-Pole of Newnham Hall,

Northamptonshire. But this again, does not confirm a Gell provenance, as numerous Chandos-Pole paintings were also part of the same collection.[18]

John Hamilton Mortimer is one of the most innovative and impressive history painters of the mid-eighteenth century. In this precautious early self-portrait, Mortimer demonstrates his ability as a painter. A powerful, unfinished work, the portrait looks ahead to Mortimer's great series of self-portraits. Its provenance also ties the portrait to one of Mortimer's most important projects and to his long standing friend, Joseph Wright of Derby shedding important light on their work together.

NOTES

1   Eds. Kenneth Garlick and Angus Macintyre, *The Diary of Joseph Farington*, New Haven and London, 1979, vol.III, p.893.

2   For Reynolds's work in Hudson's studio see Mark Hallett, *Reynolds Portraiture in Action*, New Haven and London, 2014, pp.36–38.

3   John Sutherland, 'John Hamilton Mortimer: His Life and Works', *The Walpole Society*, vol. LII, 1986, cat. no's 1, 2, 3 and 6, 7.

4   John Sutherland, 'John Hamilton Mortimer: His Life and Works', *The Walpole Society*, vol. LII, 1986, p.121.

5   Quoted in John Sutherland, 'John Hamilton Mortimer: His Life and Works', *The Walpole Society*, vol.LII, 1986, p.7.

6   This self-portrait has been variously dated to 1751 and 1757. Judy Egerton followed David Fraser in suggesting the earlier dating, although Nicholson's dating to Wright's second period in Hudson's studio is equally as plausible. See Judy Egerton, *Wright of Derby*, exh.cat., London (Tate Gallery), 1990, p.34.

7   John Sutherland, 'John Hamilton Mortimer: His Life and Works', *The Walpole Society*, vol. LII, 1986, cat.no.7.

8   John Sutherland, 'John Hamilton Mortimer: His Life and Works', *The Walpole Society*, vol. LII, 1986, cat. no's, 48 & 49.

9   John Sutherland, 'John Hamilton Mortimer: His Life and Works', *The Walpole Society*, vol. LII, 1986, cat. no's 32a and 32.

10 Quoted in Matthew Hargraves, *Candidates for Fame: The Society of Artists of Great Britain 1760–1791*, New Haven and London, 2005, p.102.

11 On the basis of a partial label on the stretcher which read: 'Sir Joshua Reynolds/ painted by himself/ Said to have been / painted during/ a visit [paper torn] opton.'

12 Benedict Nicolson, *Joseph Wright of Derby*, New Haven and London, 1968, vol.I, pp.62–63.

13 See Benedict Nicolson, *John Hamilton Mortimer ARA 1740–1779*, exh.cat., Eastbourne and London (Towner Art Gallery and Kenwood), 1968, cat.no.32, p.27.

14 Benedict Nicolson, *John Hamilton Mortimer ARA 1740–1779*, exh.cat., Eastbourne and London (Towner Art Gallery and Kenwood), 1968, cat.no.32, p.27.

15 David Manning, *Sir Joshua Reynolds: A Complete Catalogue of his Paintings*, New Haven and London, 2000, p.48, no.13c.

16 *Candid Observations on the Principal Performances Now Exhibiting at the New Room of the Society of Artists, Near Exeter-Change, Intended as a Vade Mecum to that Exhibition*, 1772, p.17.

17 David Manning, *Sir Joshua Reynolds: A Complete Catalogue of his Paintings*, New Haven and London, 2000, no.713, p.213.

18 Most of the contents of Newnham Hall was sold at Christie's, 11 July 1994, but the present painting was not included. Amongst the contents of the house were several portraits of Colonel John Chandos-Pole and his family attributed to Wright of Derby, see for example lots 214 and 216.

PAUL SANDBY RA 1731–1809

The Walking Stationer:
Memorandum books a penny a piece of the poor blind, God bless you pity the blind

Pencil, pen and black ink and watercolour,
indented for transfer
Watermark: Britannia
7½ × 5⅜ inches · 191 × 137 mm
Drawn 1760

COLLECTIONS
Brian Sewell, to 2016.

LITERATURE
John Bonehill and Stephen Daniels, *Paul
Sandby: Picturing Britain*, exh.cat., London
(Royal Academy of Arts), 2010, pp.11–139;
Ann V, Gunn, *The Prints of Paul Sandby
(1731–1809), A Catalogue Raisonné*, London,
2015, cat.no.162, p.191;
ENGRAVED: by Paul Sandby for the *Twelve
London Cries from the Life*, Part 1, etching,
published London, 1760.

This unusually sensitively characterised drawing was made by Paul Sandby in preparation for a projected series of engravings recording the *Cries* of London. Sandby's drawing of a *Walking Stationer* was turned into an etching published as part of *Twelve London Cries done from the Life* in 1760. Sandby's project fitted into a graphic tradition of recording the itinerant trades of London, Marcellus Laroon having published a series of *Cryes of the City of London* in 1688. Sandby's prints and their associated drawings have been the subject of much scholarly debate and this previously unpublished sheet offers a new perspective on the process and techniques of Sanby's project.[1]

Sandby trained initially as a military draughtsman and was involved in the Survey of Scotland, the project charged with making maps of the highlands, as part of the campaign to restore peace in the area after the rising of 1745. The *Cries* date from before his maturity as a landscape painting, suggesting that he was attempting to forge a career by working for the London print trade. Sets of engravings of itinerant tradesmen and performers had been popular in Europe for centuries; in 1688 Marcellus Laroon the Elder first published his *Cryes of the City of London*, which proved so popular that they were regularly re-issued throughout the eighteenth century. As Bonehill and Daniels have suggested, it was a revised and 'improved' set of the Laroon plates made by Louis-Phillippe Boitard in a consciously French manner and

The Walking Stationer · Le Libraire ambulant.
Memorandum books a penny a piece of the Poor blind, · Ayez pitie du pauvre Aveugle, achetés ses
God bless you pity the Blind. · petits Livrets et que bon Dieu vous benisse.

Paul Sandby
The Walking Stationer, 1760
Etching · 8½ × 6⅛ inches · 216 × 154 mm
© The Trustees of the British Museum

published in the 1750s which may actually have prompted Sandby to execute his series. Boitard updated the costumes and faces of Laroon's plates, introducing models borrowed from François Boucher, the resulting figures were felt to be too refined and elegant to be realistic, so when Sandby executed his series, he made a point of emphasising that his figures were 'done from life.'

This compelling study of *The Walking Stationer* was published with the lines: 'Memorandum books a penny a piece of the Poor blind/ God bless you pity the Blind' and in French: 'Le Libraire embulant/ Ayer pitié du pauvre Aveugle, achetter/ ses petis Livrès et que bon Dieu vous benisse.'[2] Showing a blind man holding a basket of books and being guided by a young boy, the composition is one of Sandby's most compelling. Sandby has removed all extraneous details – landscape, other figures or paraphernalia of the trade – concentrating on the figure of the Stationer and his young guide, who looks out at the viewer.

Though Sandby only issued twelve etchings of the *Cries* over seventy watercolour drawings by Sandby exist for the project.[3] Seventy-six of these drawings were sold at Christie's in 1965 from the collection of Lord Bruce and show as John Bonehill and Stephen Daniels have suggested 'a considerable degree of stylistic and technical diversity.'[4] In fact many of the drawings from the Bruce album are fairly crude in execution suggesting that they were preliminary studies, which Sandby then refined before he prepared the etching. The Bruce album study for the plate of '*My pretty little Gimy Tarters*' (Yale Center for British Art), shows the figure rapidly blocked in with

only a schematic treatment of the street scene which appears behind the figure in the published print. This sheet, by contrast, isconsiderably closer to its related etching. It is therefore possible that this beautifully rendered study, which Sandby prepared first in black chalk and then worked up in ink and watercolour, was made as the model for the final etching, a possibility given further weight by the indentations for transfer to the plate.

It is possible that Sandby published no further groups of these etchings because he was increasingly lucratively occupied with painting landscape both in gouache and watercolour, as well as in oils. In 1760 he showed two oils, including the fine *View of Lord Harcourt's Seat at Newnham*, and three watercolours at the first exhibition of the Society of Artists.

After Marcellus Laroon II
Pretty Maids Pretty Pinns Pretty Woman
From *The Cryes of the City of London Drawne after the Life* published by Piece Tempest, 1688
Etching and engraving · 9¾ × 6⅜ inches · 247 × 161 mm
© The Trustees of the British Museum

NOTES

1   See for example eds. John Bonehill and Stephen Daniels, *Paul Sandby: Picturing Britain*, exh.cat., London (Royal Academy of Arts), 2010, pp.11–139.

2   See Ann V, Gunn, *The Prints of Paul Sandby (1731–1809), A Catalogue Raisonné*, London, 2015, cat.no.162, p.191.

3   See See Ann V, Gunn, *The Prints of Paul Sandby (1731–1809), A Catalogue Raisonné*, London, 2015, cat.no.162, p.188 and Christie's, 27 April 1965, lots 58–63.

4   See for example eds. John Bonehill and Stephen Daniels, *Paul Sandby: Picturing Britain*, exh.cat., London (Royal Academy of Arts), 2010, p.136

ANTONIO ZUCCHI 1726–1795

A Classical Cappricio

Drawn with the brush in brown and grey wash, heightened with white.
18⅝ × 24 inches · 473 × 610 mm
Signed and dated in brown ink, lower right: *ant. Zucchi / 1776*
verso and inside verso: *Sketch by Anthony Zucchi ARA, husband of Angelica Kauffman, from the collection of Paul Sandby RA Chaloner Smith collection bought at Sotheby's 1890*

COLLECTIONS
Antonio Poggi (fl. *c.*1769 – after 1803);
Poggi sale, Christie 19 June, 1782, lot 84, £9.9s, bt. Sandby;
Paul Sandby (1731–1809), Lugt no.2112;
John Chaloner Smith (1827–1895);
Chaloner Smith sale, Sotheby, 14 April 1890 (and thirteen succeeding days);
Private collection, UK, acquired at the above sale;
Private collection, 2016.

This bold composition was drawn by Antonio Zucchi in 1776, and was made whilst he was working for James and Robert Adam, helping to create some of the most iconic neo-classical interiors of the late eighteenth century. Zucchi's scenographic paintings – large-scale ruinscapes – were designed as the perfect complimentary decoration for the Adams' classical rooms. This impressive sheet perfectly illustrates the composite approach to antiquity which lay at the heart of the Adams' architecture and which Zucchi learnt alongside the Adam brothers in Rome working in the orbit of Giovanni-Battista Piranesi and Charles Louis Clérisseau.

Zucchi was born in Venice, the son of Francesco Zucchi an engraver. He trained with Amigoni in Venice, where he practiced as a history painter, being elected a member of the Accademia di Pittore e Scultore in 1759. Zucchi seems first to have met James Adam in 1760 when he is recorded visiting Pola with James and his drawing-master, Clérisseau. In 1763 Zucchi painted an impressive portrait of James Adam surrounded by classical sculpture and a model of a capital from 'the British order', which James had designed for a projected new parliament building. James, on the eve of his departure from Italy, tried to persuade Zucchi, whom he described in a letter home as 'a worthy honest lad, a most singular character', to join the Adam office in London.[1]

In 1766 Zucchi did travel to London with his brother Giuseppe to work for the Adams. Zucchi became the chief decorative painter producing illustrations from Homer and Virgil for ceilings, arabesque work and most impressively, large landscape capriccios. The present grand drawing was almost certainly made in preparation for an Adam interior. In 1776 Zucchi was in the midst of producing ruinscapes for Sir Rowland Winn at Nostell Priory, delivering four large paintings for the upper hall.[2] Whilst the present sheet does not relate directly to the finished paintings, it was precisely the kind of composition Zucchi was being commissioned to execute for the Adam brothers. This composition includes a number of ruinous antique buildings: on the right a triumphal arch, in the middle-distance a bridge and on the left a grand equestrian sculpture, loosely based on one of the Dioscuri from the Quirinal hill. Arranged in the foreground, Zucchi has placed a frieze of classically dressed figures playing musical instruments, drinking and suggestive of Arcadian ease. Broadly handled in black and bistre wash highlighted with touches of white gouache, the drawing is a perfect distillation of the picturesque approach to antiquity which the Adam brothers made central to their architecture.

This type of ruinscape reflected the influence of the Adams' drawing master in Rome, the French painter and architect, Charles Louis Clérisseau. Clérisseau produced numerous architectural capriccios based upon his scrupulous observation and understanding of the remains of antiquity. The privileging of the fragment also reflected the work of Giovani Battista Piranesi and it is clear that Zucchi's work was inspired by Piranesi's philosophy. In compositions such as this Zucchi was presenting the sources of the antique ornament that the Adam brothers were using in their architecture.

Zucchi was elected an associate of the Royal Academy in 1770 designed the frontispiece for *The Works in Architecture of Robert and James Adam* (1773). Zucchi's drawings, like those of Clérisseau, were popular amongst collectors during the eighteenth century. The present sheet belonged to the publisher and fan-maker Antonio Poggi. Poggi was a friend of Zucchi's wife,

Angelica Kauffman and he was responsible for publishing a large number of her compositions as stipple engravings for use in decorative work.[3] The present drawing was included in his sale at Christie's in 1782 where it and another drawing made £9.9s, it was acquired by the landscape painter Paul Sandby. Sandby was a major collector and dealer in drawings, particularly of drawings by his contemporaries and fellow members of the Royal Academy. In the nineteenth century the drawing passed into the collection of the great print-collector and scholar John Chaloner Smith.

NOTES

1   Edinburgh, National Register of Scotland, Clerk of Penicuik Papers, Clerk MSS, GD 18/4955.
2   Eileen Harris, *The Genius of Robert Adam: His Interiors*, New Haven and London, 2001, p.205.
3   Ed. Wendy Wassyng Roworth, *Angelica Kauffman: A Continental Artist in Georgian England*, London, 1992, pp.169–170.

Antonio Zucchi
Capriccio with the Ruins of a Triumphal Arch and a Bridge, c.1776
Oil on canvas · 82¼ × 94⅛ inches · 209 × 239 mm
© National Trust Images, Nostell Priory

ANTONIO ZUCCHI 1726–1795

A Roman Ruin

Pen and brush and brown ink, black chalk.
The framing line in brown pen
16⅛ × 20½ inches · 410 × 520 mm
Signed and dated in brown pen lower right:
ant:Zucchi 1788.

This characteristic wash drawing by
Antonio Zucchi was made in the late 1780s
towards the end of his life when he had
settled with his wife, Angelica Kauffman,
in Rome. Zucchi had begun his career in
the international artistic circles in Rome,
where he worked with the architects Robert
and James Adam and their French drawing
master, Charles-Louis Clérisseau. Clérisseau
had been a pupil of the ruin-scape painter,
Giovanni Paolo Pannini and had been a
pensionnaire at the French Academy in
Rome, although he had fallen out with its
director, Charles-Joseph Natoire. The Adam
brothers and Clérisseau were amongst the
most innovative neo-classical designers of
the mid-eighteenth century, through them
Zucchi acquired a fascination with ruins; in
his most successful compositions, such as
this sheet, Zucchi recast antique fragments
into innovative new compositions which
point to the modern application of the
classical past.

Zucchi was born in Venice, but trained
largely in Rome. Once in the orbit of the
Adam brothers and Clérisseau, Zucchi
became an important member of their circle
and he is frequently credited with adding the
figures to Clérisseau's gouache ruinscapes.
These highly imaginative capriccios were
a sort after commodity across Europe;
Catherine the Great owned a large number.
Zucchi travelled to Britain to work in the
Adam practice in London in 1766. There
he was largely responsible for painting

the fantastical ruinscapes which decorate
many of Robert Adam's interiors. In 1781 he
married the painter Angelica Kauffman and
shortly afterwards they returned to Italy. In
Rome he managed her burgeoning business,
handling many of the commissions from
visiting European, predominantly British
aristocrats. At the same time he continued
to produce finished drawings of ruinscapes
such as this example, which is signed and
dated 1788.

This boldly conceived composition
is partly indebted to the work Zucchi
completed with Clérisseau, but shows a
grander artistic influence, namely the prints
of Giovanni Battista Piranesi. The ambitious scenographic view shows what looks
like a partially ruined Roman tomb, with
a projected portico and connecting bridge.

The form of the tomb, with the arcaded
basement, niches on the central section with
the heavy, projecting entablature and brick
arches above covered in vegetation all recall
Piranesi's view of the so-called Tempio della
Tosse near Tivoli which was published as
a plate in his *Vedute di Roma* in the 1760s.
During the eighteenth-century the tomb was
considered to be the remains of a temple
and so Zucchi has imaginatively attached a
grand composite portico, reminiscent of the
Pantheon and connecting bridge, to create an
imaginative reconstruction. As such, Zucchi's
drawings point to the modernity of the fragment and the ruin in contemporary European
architecture and design. Preserved in excellent condition, this late design underscores
Zucchi's importance in the neo-classical
circles of Adam, Clérisseau and Piranesi.

Giovanni Battista Piranesi
*Veduta del Tempio, detto della Tosse su la Via Tiburtina,
un miglio vicino a Tivoli,* 1760–78
Etching · 17½ × 22¾ inches · 444 × 576 mm
© The Trustees of the British Museum

ALEXANDER COZENS *c.*1717–1786

A landscape of the imagination

Pen and ink with grey and black washes on
prepared yellow paper,
within the artist's wash-line mount
3¼ × 6⅜ inches · 107 × 163 mm
Inscribed: *4th stile of composition* and signed
on the mount
Drawn *c.*1770

COLLECTIONS
Sir Bruce Ingram (1877-1963);
Lowell Libson Ltd;
Private collection, UK, to 2015.

EXHIBITED
London, Lowell Libson Ltd, Watercolours
and Drawings 18th and 19th Centuries, 2004,
no.1.

This boldly worked ink drawing was made
by Alexander Cozens according to the
rules he adumbrated in his 'New Method'.
A successful drawing master and landscape
painter, Cozens provided a system whereby
apparently accidental 'blots' were developed
into highly refined classical landscapes.
Aimed at amateurs, the 'New Method'
codified much of the intellectual underpin-
ning of professional painters of the period,
such as Thomas Gainsborough.[1] In the

Alexander Cozens *4th Stile of Composition*, from
An essay to facilitate the inventing of landscape, 1759
Etching · 3⅞ × 6 inches · 99 × 153 mm
© The Trustees of the British Museum

present beautifully worked drawing, Cozens
has developed an initial blot drawing with
the brush to produce a complex and highly
structured landscape.

Alexander Cozens's first drawing
manual was published in 1759: *An Essay to
Facilitate the Inventing of Landskips, Intended
for Students in the Art*.[2] In the two-page
explanatory essay he began with a passage
from the 1724 English edition of Leonardo
da Vinci's *Treatise on Painting*, which
described how invention of composition
might be assisted by looking at accidents
of nature, such as old walls covered with
dirt or streaked stones. Cozens explained
that a happy accident with an adept pupil
had led him to improve upon Leonardo by
creating those imperfect forms on purpose
with some degree of design, and then using
them as the basis for landscape compositions. These 'rude black Sketches' or 'blots'
were drawn swiftly with a brush dipped in
Indian ink, from which hints were taken
for the outline of a landscape drawn on
a clean piece of post paper laid on top. In
A New Method he explained that 'an artificial
blot is a production of chance, with a small
degree of design' and should be embarked
on only after the practitioners had possessed
their minds 'strongly with the subject'. He
defines the 'true blot' as 'an assemblage of
dark shapes or masses made with ink upon
a piece of paper, and likewise of light ones
produced by the paper being left blank.'[3]
He provided eight pairs of blots and outline
landscapes drawn from them as examples
of the eight styles of composition, which he
listed in the essay.

Cozens's 'blot' technique was fully
evolved by the 1750s, but he did not explain
it in detail until the publication of *A New*

*Method of Assisting the Invention in Drawing
Original Compositions of Landscape* in 1786. The
pencil inscription on this drawing indicates
that Cozens' related this landscape to the
fourth in his 'Descriptions of the various
Kinds of Composition of Landscape' which
he appended to the *New Method*. The descriptions offered brief classifications for types of
landscapes. The fourth is described as: 'A flat
of a circular form, bounded by groups of
objects, at a moderate distance from the eye.'[4]
It is clear the drawing is derived from a blot,
the simple areas of wash have been elaborated
by the use of a brush, the method for the
creation of such studies Cozens labelled as:
'a Sketch from a Blot with a Hair Pencil, as a
Preparation for a Finished Drawing.' The small
sheet also shows evidence of the use of a read
pen – in the tree in the middle-distance – and
it is clear that he regarded it as a successful development, because the drawing was
carefully mounted, inscribed and signed by
Cozens himself.

Preserved in excellent condition, this small,
intense study provides powerful evidence
of the systematic approach to landscape
drawing which Cozens developed towards
the end of his career. Fluidly worked in rich,
Indian ink this concentrated study points to
both the eighteenth century fascination with
the rational world of classification and the
emotional potential of the irrational accident.

NOTES
1 For Cozens see Kim Sloan, *Alexander and John
   Robert Cozens: The Poetry of Landscape*, New
   Haven and London, 1986, pp.36–62.
2 Alexander Cozens, *A New Method of Landscape*,
   London, 1786, pp.6–7.
3 Alexander Cozens, *A New Method of Landscape*,
   London, 1786, pp.6–7.
4 Alexander Cozens, *A New Method of Landscape*,
   London, 1786, p.32.

ANTON von MARON 1733–1808

Two Academic Nudes

[A] OPPOSITE
Black and white chalk on paper
20¾ × 15½ inches · 527 × 394 mm
Signed, inscribed and dated, lower centre:
Maron del Romae 1776

[B] REPRODUCED OVERLEAF
Black and white chalk on paper
20¾ × 15½ inches · 527 × 394 mm

COLLECTION
Private collection, New York, 2016.

Joseph Charles Natoire
Life class at the Academie Royale, Paris, 1746
Watercolour and black chalk
17¾ × 12¾ inches · 453 × 323 mm
© The Samuel Courtauld Trust, The Courtauld
Gallery, London

These boldly handled life studies were made by the Austrian painter Anton von Maron for use at Anton Raphael Mengs's private academy in Rome in 1776. Maron was Mengs's principal assistant and deputised for Mengs in Rome whilst Mengs was working in Madrid for Charles III of Spain between 1773 and 1777. These previously unpublished, large-scale life drawings are an important addition to Maron's oeuvre and offer unprecedented evidence of the mechanics of the international Roman art world in the second half of the eighteenth century.

Maron was born in Vienna where he was initially trained, from 1755 he was based in Rome where he lived in Mengs's house on via Sistina; until 1761 he was Mengs's pupil and studio assistant. Two joint commissions for frescoes in Rome are known from this period: the ceiling of the church S. Eusebio and the *Parnassus* at Villa Albani and it seems to have been Maron's aptitude at working in fresco which enabled Mengs to successfully complete these projects.[1] The two painters remained close and Maron's mature works show evidence of his debt to Mengs. Maron eventually married Mengs's sister, Therese Concodia, a successful miniature painter. Mengs's summons to Madrid in 1761 entailed a fundamental change in Maron's position as an artist in Rome. He now ran Mengs's studio, together with the Würzbug court painter Christoph Fesel, and was the agent for Mengs's affairs in Rome. As a result Maron assumed an important position within the Roman art world, completing a sequence of imposing portraits of British, Austrian and German Grand Tourists and producing a number of historical paintings for travellers. During the 1770s Maron became the official portraitist to the Hapsburg Court in Vienna and in 1772 he was ennobled for his services to the Imperial Court. Maron was also successful within the domestic art market of Rome and his most ambitious project was the completion of a multi-figure mythological cycle based on the story of Aeneas that the artist executed in 1784–85 for the Casino in the Villa Borghese.

By the 1770s the Roman art world was well served by academic and semi-academic institutions; the city itself was one of the centres of artistic education in the world and attracted an international roster of young painters who came to complete their training. These included the Académie de France à Rome and the Accademia di San Luca, along with a series of informal evening drawing academies held by Rome's leading artists.[2] The Accademia del Disegno – known more usually as the Accademia Capitolina del Nudo – was established under the aegis of the Accademia di San Luca in 1754 by Benedict XIV in a large room below the Pinacoteca Capitolina in the Palazzo dei Conservatori. The direction of the students and model was entrusted to a rotating group of artists appointed by the president, both Mengs and Maron supervised the life drawing exercises. Maron, like Mengs, was also much involved in the organisation of the Accademia di San Luca and was responsible for producing a number of the official portraits of its most members.[3]

By the 1770s young artists of any nationality seeking a private drawing academy in Rome could choose from at least a dozen, the most famous were those run by Pompeo Batoni and Mengs in their own houses. The German painter Johann Gottlieb Puhlmann left a series of descriptions of Batoni's private academy from the mid-1770s.

Maron del: Roma 1776

In a letter of 20 January 1775, Puhlmann described his experience:

In our living room we now have an iron brazier, and thus have a warm room when we come home from the academy, where I have the good fortune of sitting to the left of Cavalier Pompeo, who points out my mistakes and is satisfied with my work. I have now drawn ten figures from life and copied twenty-two drawings. The dear man gives us everything that we ask of him, and when the academy has concluded he discourses informally about some aspects of painting.[4]

There is considerable evidence that Mengs was also keenly interested in teaching and particularly the method of learning from the life model. Some insight into Mengs's method can be discerned from the large number of drawings he made in the early 1770s that survive. A series of eight drawings preserved in Karlsruhe in the Staatliche Kunsthalle, Graphische Sammlung, seem to have been assembled by Mengs for the purpose of demonstrating the different approaches to the male nude of Michelangelo and Raphael. In addition, as Steffi Roettgen has noted, he endowed these nude studies with different thematic meanings, differentiating between a Herculean and a Bacchic type, and between an Apollonian, an Adonic, and an Antonius-like type.[5]

It is in this pedagogic context that our two studies by Maron should be read. One is prominently signed and dated 'Romae 1776' underlining that this was not the work of Maron as a student, but as a celebrated painter who was in charge of Mengs's private academy in his absence. The sheets are close to Mengs's mature academy drawings in style and technique: drawn on large sheets of Roman paper in black chalk heightened in white. The setting of the male figure in both sheets recalls those by Mengs at Karlsruhe. Whilst the arrangement of the models also recall famous figures from the work of earlier masters. The signed and

dated sheet shows the model seated, with his arms over his head in a pose based upon one of Michelangelo's *ignudi* supporting the scene of the *Sacrifice of Noah* from the Sistine Ceiling. The second figure shows Maron posing the model in the character of the lead executioner from Raphael's *Massacre of the Innocents*. The drawings were therefore devised as a pairing of contrasting types, life models animating the works of Michelangelo and Raphael to exemplify their different approaches to the human figure.

These two important drawings join a small group of seven life drawings by Maron which survive in the collection of the Biblioteca civica in Fermo, in Le Marche.[6] But unlike the group at Fermo, which are largely dated to 1772 and derived from drawings by Mengs, these two drawings seem to have been prepared by Maron himself for use by students after Mengs's departure for Spain. The grand drawings have a pictorial effect which is derived from the emphasis on the musculature and the intensive play of light and shade on the surface, cleverly communicated by the use of black and white chalks. As life drawings, made by Maron at the height of his career, these bold sheets offer important insights into the educational mechanics of private academies in Rome at a moment when a concentration of British and other European artists were present in the city. Rome was a major educational centre for an emerging generation of European neo-classicism, artists as various as Jacques Louis David, Tobias Sergel and Henry Fuseli, all passed through Mengs's academy and would undoubtedly have seen and been encouraged to copy these sheets.

Anton von Maron
Seated nude with raised arm
Pencil and white chalk on grey prepared paper
20¾ × 15⅝ inches · 528 × 395 mm
Inscribed *Maron da Meng* and dated *7 ma 1772*
Biblioteca Comunale, Fermo

NOTES

1 For Maron see Isabella Schmittmann, *Anton von Maron (1731–1808) Leben und Werk*, Munich, 2013 and Antonello Cesareo, *Studi su Anton von Maron 2001–2012*, Rome, 2014.
2 For academies in Rome in this period see Edgar Peters Bowron, 'Academic Life Drawing in Rome, 1750–1790', in eds. Richard Campbell and Victor Carlson, *Visions of Antiquity: Neoclasscal Figure Drawings*, exh.cat., Los Angeles (Los Angeles County Museum), 1993, pp.75–85.
3 For Maron and the Accademia di san Luca see Antonello Cesareo, 'Anton von Maron e l'Accademia di San Luca' in *Studi del Settecento Romano*, vol.26, 2010, pp.201–234.
4 Quoted in Edgar Peters Bowron and Peter Kerber, *Pompeo Batoni: Prince of Painters in Eighteenth-Century Rome*, New Haven and London, 2007, p.151.
5 Steffi Roettgen, *Anton Raphael Mengs 1728–1779, Leben und wirken*, Munich, 2003, vol.II, pp.303–311.
6 See Isabella Schmittmann, *Anton von Maron (1731–1808) Leben und Werk*, Munich, 2013, cat. no's. 115–119, pp.369–373.

FRANCESCO BARTOLOZZI RA 1727–1815

A young woman drawing

Black and red chalk, on laid paper
10 × 13⅝ inches · 254 × 346mm
Inscribed in a later hand,
lower left: *Bartolozzi*
Drawn 1799

ENGRAVED
By Bartolozzi for *Elements of Drawings*
by Francesco Bartolozzi RA *and Francis Vieira*
Portuensis Containing both Original Designs
and Copies from ancient Masters, published
London, 1799.

This sensitive drawing was made by
the engraver Francesco Bartolozzi in
preparation for a plate in his 1799 *Elements of*
Drawings which he published in collabora-
tion with the Portuguese painter Francisco
Vieira, known as Vieira Portuensis. The
drawing is an exceptionally rare depiction
of an amateur female artist at work copying
a life-drawing, as such, the sheet offers
important information about amateur
artistic practice at the end of the eighteenth
century. Bartolozzi, an Italian engraver
who had a celebrated and prolific career in
Britain was elected a founder member of
the Royal Academy and had a close working relationship with a number of female
artists, both professional, including Angelica
Kauffman and amateur, such as Lady Diana
Beauclerk. Bartolozzi also had a thriving
practice as an art teacher, with a roster of
celebrated amateur pupils and his *Elements*

of Drawings was directed towards instruction
of amateur artists.

This beautifully worked sheet in black
chalk, heightened with red chalk, shows a
woman seated at a drawing board copying
a life study of a seated nude figure. The
sheet being copied appears to be after a
life drawing: women were still excluded
from studying in the life academy at the
Royal Academy. As Kim Sloan has pointed
out, Bartolozzi's image is exceptional, as
'relatively few drawings resulting from
such studies by female amateurs exist.'[1]
Bartolozzi's drawing had an obvious
pedagogic purpose, to show amateur artists
the importance of copying as an educational
exercise; the *Elements of Drawings* was made
up of engravings after old master paintings
that could be copied to improve students'
drawing skills.

As an image of a woman at work, copying a male life-drawing, this sheet presents
an exceptional depiction of an amateur
female artist in the late eighteenth century.
Bartolozzi's refined technique – the use
of red and black chalks – approximates his
celebrated use of stipple engraving, whilst
the design itself, the complex arrangement
of the young woman's hair and profile,
echoes Bartolozzi's successful career producing prints and designs for Wedgwood.

NOTE
1   Kim Sloan, *A Noble Art: Amateur Artists and*
    Drawing Masters c.1600–1800, exh.cat., London
    (British Museum), 2000, p.213.

Francesco Bartolozzi
Young woman copying a life drawing
from *Elements of Drawings by* Francesco Bartolozzi
and Francis Vieira Portuensis, 1799
Stipple engraving · 13¾ × 18⅝ inches · 350 × 475 mm
© The Trustees of the British Museum

HENRY FUSELI, RA 1741–1825

A captive woman

Black chalks, on buff-coloured paper
18⅛ × 12⅜ inches · 459 × 315 mm
Stamped verso: *Baroness Norths Collection / of Drawings by H Fuseli Esq.*
Drawn *c.*1781

COLLECTIONS
Sir Thomas Lawrence, who acquired the contents of Fuseli's studio;
Susan, Countess of Guilford, née Coutts (1771–1837), acquired from the Lawrence estate;
Susan, Baroness North (1797–1884), daughter of the above;
Mrs A. M. Jaffé, acquired in France, *c.*1950 to 2016.

This boldly drawn sheet depicting a seated figure was made by Fuseli at an important and highly productive moment in his career. The monumental drawing is closely related to another sheet by Fuseli in the British Museum which Schiff published as subject unknown.[1] Both drawings were made when Fuseli was designing his most important sequence of historical works, including scenes from Shakespeare and Milton, *The Nightmare* and *The Death of Dido* which was exhibited at the Royal Academy to great critical acclaim in 1781. The present drawing does not relate directly to any of Fuseli's finished historical paintings of the period, but evidently the image of a slightly menacing, seated and covered old woman was precisely the sort of motif he was playing with. It is notable that the same figure reappears later in Fuseli's work as the witch from Ben Jonson's *Witch's Song* which Fuseli produced as both a painting and engraving in 1812.

Fuseli returned to London in 1779 from a highly creative and productive period in Rome and established himself as one of the leading history painters of the period. Fuseli re-established contact with his old mentor Sir Joshua Reynolds, becoming a regular guest at his dinner table and visitor to his studio. The earliest and most striking manifestation of this strategy was Fuseli's *Death of Dido*, exhibited in 1781 at the Royal Academy. Executed on the same scale as Reynolds's version (Royal Collection), Fuseli's vertically oriented picture was hung directly opposite Reynolds's with its horizontal orientation, inevitably inviting comparison between the two works and garnering Fuseli much publicity and favourable reviews in the newspapers.

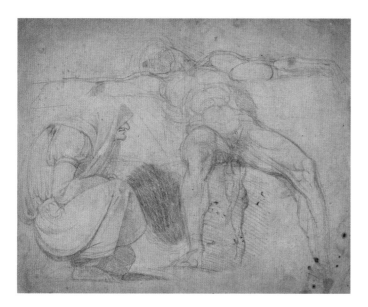

Henry Fuseli
Here identified as a study of the Death of Dido 1781?
Black chalk · 21 × 25¾ inches · 532 × 655 mm
© The Trustees of the British Museum

Henry Fuseli
The Witch and the Mandrake, 1812
Soft-ground etching · 17 × 21⅞ inches · 430 × 556 mm
© The Trustees of the British Museum

The present, previously unpublished sheet, relates closely to a drawing now in the British Museum. That sheet shows the same seated old woman, drawn on a smaller scale and more schematic in design, seated next to an anatomical drawing of a man. The pose of this figure is related to the pose of Dido in his *Death of Dido*; the foreshortened torso, arrangement of head, oblique view of *Dido's* features and arms all suggest that the study can be viewed as an initial thought for the composition. Fuseli may have initially thought of including the figure of the hunched and covered old woman. Drawn on identical paper to the British Museum sheet, our study is an enlarged depiction of the same figure, more elaborately delineated and developed. The presence of a chain to the right of the figure, suggests that the iconography was related in some way to a scene of imprisonment.

Fuseli had first explored the motif of the hooded old woman in an early Roman drawing, *The Venus Seller*.[2] The idea of a grotesque old woman, hooded and with

angular nose and projecting chin seen in profile was most spectacularly used by Fuseli in his sequence of paintings depicting *The Three Witches* from Macbeth.[3] Fuseli seems to have kept the present sheet and may have returned to it when preparing a painting of *The Witch and the Mandrake* from Ben Jonson's *Witch's Song* from his *Masque of Queens* in 1812.[4] Here the same seated figure looks out from under her hood and picks a mandrake by moonlight. Jonson's drama had been performed at the court of James I in 1609, inspired the subject. To throw the nobility of the queens into relief, the poet added a coven of witches, one of whom declares: 'I last night lay all alone, On the ground, to hear the mandrake groan; And plucked him up, though he grew full low, And, as I had done, the cock did crow.' The figure was reversed in the associated etching which was published in 1812.[5] It seems likely that the present drawing remained as part of Fuseli's working archive of figure studies.

The present drawing was presumably purchased with the bulk of Fuseli's drawings

after the artist's death by Sir Thomas Lawrence. Lawrence's large group of Fuseli drawings were then acquired by Susan, Countess of Guildford (1771–1837). Lady Guildford was the eldest daughter of the banker Thomas Coutts (1735–1822), who himself had supported Fuseli's journey to Rome in the 1770s and had remained one of the artist's key patrons. In 1796 Susan married George, 3rd Earl of Guildford, whose father was Prime Minister of Great Britain between 1770 and 1782. She was a close friend of Fuseli and during her lifetime assembled a large and important collection of his work.

NOTES

1   Gert Schiff, *Johann Heinrich Füssli 1741–1825*, Munich, 1973, vol.II, cat.no.834.
2   Schiff, op.cit., cat.no.655.
3   Schiff, op.cit., cat.no.733–735.
4   Schiff, op.cit., cat.no.1497.
5   D. H. Weinglass, *Prints and Engraved Illustrations by and After Henry Fuseli: A Catalogue Raisonné*, Aldershot, 1990, cat. no.291, pp.335–6.

JOHN RUSSELL RA 1745–1806

George White, bust-length, as Saint Peter

Pastel
23½ × 17¼ inches · 596 × 438 mm
Signed and dated lower right:
J Russell/ fecit 1772

COLLECTIONS
Russell sale, Christie's, 14 February 1807:
'John Russell, Esq., RA deceased, crayon
painter to His Majesty, the Prince of Wales,
and Duke of York; and brought from his late
Dwelling in Newman Street', lot 92,
'St Peter', bt. Thompson (1½ guineas);
Anonymous sale; Sotheby's, London,
25 September 1980, lot 113;
Private collection, UK, 2016.

LITERATURE
Martin Postle, 'Patriarchs, prophets and
paviours: Reynolds's images of old age',
The Burlington Magazine, vol.CXXX, no.1027,
October 1988, pp.739–40, fig.9;
Martin Postle, *Sir Joshua Reynolds: The Subject
Pictures*, Cambridge, 1995, p.136, repr.;
Neil Jeffares, *Dictionary of pastellists before
1800*, online edition, J.64.2928.

John Russell was admitted to the Royal
Academy in March 1770, at the same time
as Daniel Gardner.[1] The nascent Academy
Schools were still establishing their teaching
structures, but central to the syllabus were
the twin components of drawing after the
antique and from life models. By 1772 Russell
had already been awarded a silver medal
and progressed to the life academy, where
he produced this remarkable pastel study of
George White. White was the most famous
model employed by the Royal Academy
and prominent artists in the second half
of the eighteenth century. A paviour – or
street mender –by profession White had
been discovered by Joshua Reynolds, who
in turn introduced him to the Academy.
Russell's striking head study demonstrates
his abilities as a portraitist and pastellist, at

the same time showing his interest in the
Academy's preoccupation with promoting
history painting.

George White was one of the most
celebrated models in eighteenth-
century London. According to the painter
Joseph Moser:

*Old George…owed the ease in which he passed
his latter days, in a great measure to Sir Joshua
Reynolds, who found him exerting himself in
the laborious employment of thumping down
stones in the street; and observing not only the
grand and majestic traits of his countenance,
but the dignity of his muscular figure, took him
out of a situation to which his strength was
by no means equal, clothed, fed, and had him,
first as a model in his own painting room, then
introduced him as a subject for the students of
the Royal Academy.*[2]

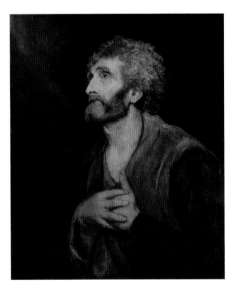

Sir Joshua Reynolds
*Dionysius Areopagite, a nobleman of Athens and
disciple of St Paul, c.1772*
Oil on canvas · 30 × 25 inches · 763 × 635 mm
Private collection (formerly with Lowell Libson Ltd)

Isaac Jehner, after Reynolds
Dionysius Areopagita
Mezzotint
Published 15 November 1776
10 × 7⅝ inches · 254 × 193 mm
© The Trustees of the British Museum

As Martin Postle has pointed out, whilst characterful studies of old men posed as biblical figures, prophets or saints by Continental old masters were readily available on the art market – Reynolds himself had copied a head of *Joab* by Federico Bencovich in the collection of his friend and patron, Lord Palmerston – finding a model in Britain from whom to execute a painting was more difficult.[3]

White therefore offered a rare opportunity for artists to combine portraiture and history painting, by painting a model in the guise of an historical or literary character. In 1771 Reynolds showed at the Royal Academy a picture of White entitled *Resignation*. It was engraved in 1772 and accompanied by a stanza from Oliver Goldsmith's *Deserted Village*, implying a literary context to what is essentially a portrait. In his annotated Royal Academy catalogue, Horace Walpole noted: 'This was an old beggar, who had so fine a head that Sir Joshua chose him for the father in his picture from Dante, and painted him several times, as did others in imitation of Reynolds. There were even cameos and busts of him.' White sat to, amongst others Johan Zoffany, John Sanders, Nathaniel Hone and the sculptor John Bacon.[4]

Russell's portrait of White is a highly charged character study. Executed in pastel, Russell's preferred medium, it shows White in the habit and attitude of St. Peter. Russell has clearly converted a life-study, made in the Royal Academy, into a historical painting. Contemporary evidence suggests that Reynolds began studies of White without a specific subject-matter in mind. His pupil, James Northcote, described the gestation of Reynolds's *Ugolino* suggesting he initially painted the head-study of White and then decided to add to the canvas to create the finished composition.[5] Russell probably began by drawing White's head, distinctive beard and hair, before adding the hands clasped in prayer and the halo. Head studies

of saints such as this, were familiar from the work of Italian seventeenth and eighteenth century painters and notable depictions of St Peter survive by Guido Reni and Pompeo Batoni amongst others. In 1772, the year Russell completed this pastel, Reynolds executed a similar profile portrait of White which he converted into a portrait entitled *Dionysius Areopagita a nobleman of Athens and disciple of St Paul* (Private collection, formerly with Lowell Libson Ltd). It maybe that Reynolds used his painting of White as a study to encourage the students of the Academy.

Preserved in outstanding condition, Russell's portrait of George White is hugely important evidence of the activities of students at the Royal Academy during its first years. This life-study offers tantalising evidence that Reynolds taught his own method of historical painting to the first generation of students at the Academy. This pastel is also a depiction of the most famous model in eighteenth century London, and as such offers invaluable evidence of the mechanics of art teaching at a critical moment in the development of British art.

Sir Joshua Reynolds
Count Ugolino and his children in the dungeon, 1770–3
Oil on canvas · 20½ × 28⅜ inches · 520 × 720 mm
Knole, Kent
© National Trust Images / Brian Tremain

Sir Joshua Reynolds
Pope Pavarius, c.1770–5
Oil on canvas · 30 × 25 inches · 762 × 635 mm
Guildhall Art Gallery, City of London

NOTES

1   Sidney C. Hutchison, 'The Royal Academy Schools, 1768–1830', *The Walpole Society*, v.38, 1962, p.135.
2   For George White see Martin Postle, 'Patriarchs, prophets, and paviours: Reynolds's images of old age', *The Burlington Magazine*, 1988, vol.cxxx, pp.736–37 and Martin Postle, *Sir Joshua Reynolds: the subject pictures*, Cambridge, 1995, pp.121–160.
3   Martin Postle, *Sir Joshua Reynolds: the subject pictures*, Cambridge, 1995, p.125.
4   For other artists who used White see: Martin Postle, 'Patriarchs, prophets, and paviours: Reynolds's images of old age', *The Burlington Magazine*, 1988, vol.cxxx, pp.739–740.
5   1818, I, pp.278–283.

GEORGE MORLAND 1763–1804

Self portrait

Black chalk with traces of red chalk
11⅜ × 8⅝ inches · 290 × 220 mm
Inscribed and dated, lower right: *George Morland 1775. Portrait of himself.*

COLLECTIONS
Sir John Charles Robinson (1824–1913);
C. J. Newton Robinson;
Private collection, France, to 2016.

'His forehead was high with the frontal veins singularly apparent when under the influence of passion or intense thought; his eyes were dark hazel, full and somewhat piercing, his nose rather aquiline… he generally wore a coat of mixed colour, with long square skirts, and breeches of velveteen; these, with two or three waistcoats and a dirty silk handkerchief round his neck, completed his appearance, which was that of a hackney-coachman.'[1]

This previously unpublished and highly refined self-portrait of the young George Morland was made in 1775 when he was 12 years old. Carefully observed in profile, the portrait shows Morland's characteristic features and messy hair. Morland was a child prodigy who exhibited his first works at the Royal Academy in 1773, he went on to have a successful career as a genre painter, subverting the normal commercial model of artists in the period to have a profitable relationship with dealers and print publishers. Morland's unconventional appearance mirrored his unconventional life and in spite of his commercial success he ended up in debt. This incisive and precocious early self-portrait underlines what an intelligent and sensitive draughtsman Morland was.

George Morland's father was the successful painter and engraver, Henry Robert Morland. Morland senior owned a house at 47 Leicester Fields, London which he sold to Joshua Reynolds in 1760. Morland therefore grew up in an ambitious and well connected artistic household; a sketch of the young Morland asleep in a chair by his father's friend Paul Sandby survives in the Royal Collection.[2] This exposure within the artistic establishment undoubtedly led to Morland's early talent in drawing being promoted. From 1775 Morland became a prolific

George Morland
Self-portrait, c.1795
Chalk · 18½ × 13 inches · 470 mm × 330 mm
© National Portrait Gallery, London

George Morland. 1775
Portrait of himself
drawn by himself

contributor to London's exhibiting society showing two sketches 'in chalks' at the Free Society in 1775 and six 'stained drawings', or watercolours, the following year.

The rediscovery of this self-portrait gives a sense of how accomplished Morland was by the time he began exhibiting at the Free Society. Drawn when Morland was only twelve years old, the profile is handled confidently, but with a number of noticeable pentiments, for example in the precise outline of the chin. The sophisticated tonal handling of the black chalk suggests Morland's training with his father, who was a celebrated pastel portraitist by this date. The sensitive characterisation, the features – 'his eyes were dark hazel, full and somewhat piercing, his nose rather aquiline' – and the unruly hair all accord with Mortland's later, extensive iconography.

Morland's iconography is worthy of note. A self-portrait, apparently painted at the same date as this drawing is in the collection of the National Portrait Gallery, London. But as Richard Walker has suggested, its confused provenance, means that the sitter's identity is little more than an historic attribution.[3] In fact the discovery of the present drawing suggests that if it is by Morland it dates from slightly early in his precocious career, as by 1775 he was an assured and mature draughtsman who had already developed his characteristic appearance. Morland as depicted in the present self-portrait is instantly identifiable as the sitter in John Raphael Smith's portrait of 1792 and Morland's own self-portrait in black chalk of 1795 in the National Portrait Gallery and in miniature at the Yale Center for British Art and even in his final, famous self-portrait *The Artist in His Studio and His Man Gibbs* painted in 1802.

At the age of fourteen Morland's official seven-year apprenticeship with his father began. As in his early years, Henry Morland tutored him with close scrutiny and encouraged him in studying anatomy and in copying the work of earlier masters. His tuition was carried out entirely at home while he worked in his father's studio as an assistant and restorer. He was not permitted to study at the Royal Academy Schools, perhaps from parental concern for his moral welfare or from his father's disregard for the validity of an academic training.

Morland went on to have a successful, if unconventional career and his self-fashioning, as Nicholas Grindle has recently suggested, remained individual and ambiguous.[4] This ambiguity makes the rediscovery of the present portrait extremely interesting, it suggests that Morland was conscious of the power of his image from an exceptionally young age; it also underscores the importance of viewing his later work and reputation in the light of his early emergence as a child prodigy. An engaging, intelligent and beautiful drawing, this self-portrait is an important addition to not only Morland's oeuvre but the genre of British self-portraiture in the eighteenth century.

NOTES

1 George *Dawe, The Life of George Morland with Remarks on his Works*, London, 1807, pp.14–15.
2 A. P. Oppé, *The Drawings of Paul and Thomas Sandby in the collection his Majesty the King at Windsor Castle*, Oxford, 1947, cat.no.373, p.78.
3 Richard Walker, *National Portrait Gallery: Regency Portraits*, London, 1985, 1., pp.345–346.
4 Nicholas Grindle, 'George Morland: In the Margins', in eds. Layla Bloom and Nicholas Grindle, *George Morland: Art, Traffic and Society in Late Eighteenth Century England*, Leeds, 2015, pp.7–22.

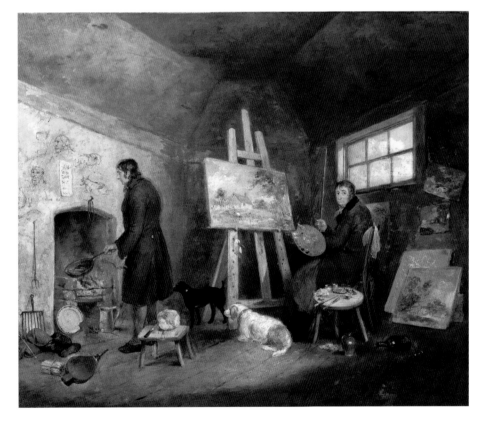

George Morland
The Artist in his studio with his man Gibbs, 1802
Oil on canvas · 25 × 30 inches · 635 × 762 mm
By permission of Nottingham City Museums & Galleries

THOMAS ROWLANDSON 1756–1827

The coach booking office: Rowlandson and Henry Wigstead booking their passage

Ink and watercolour
7 × 11½ inches · 178 × 292 mm
Verso: colour trials
Drawn c.1775.

COLLECTIONS
The Earl of Mayo;
Desmond Coke;
Coke sale, Christie's, 22 November 1929, lot 28 (to Frank Sabin);
Major Leonard Dent, acquired from Frank T. Sabin in 1939;
Dent sale, Christie's, 10 July 1984, lot 2 (to Leger Galleries);
Leger Galleries, London;
Private collection, UK, acquired 1987, to 2016.

LITERATURE
H. Faust, 'A Note on Rowlandson', *Apollo*, June 1936, repr.;
The Illustrated London News, 12 September 1936, repr. p.452;
F. Gordon Roe, *Rowlandson: The Life and Times of a British Genius*, 1947, repr. pl.XI;
R. R. Wark, *Rowlandson's Drawings for a Tour in a Post Chaise*, 1963, San Marino, p.13 note;
L. M. E. Dent, *Hillfields: Notes on the Contents*, 1972, p.19;
John Hayes, *The Art of Thomas Rowlandson*, Alexandria, 1990, pp.58–59;
Lowell Libson, Hugh Belsey, John Basket, et al, *Beauty and the Beast: A loan exhibition of Rowlandson's works from British private collections*, 2007, pp.74–5.

EXHIBITED
London, Frank T. Sabin, *Watercolour drawings by Thomas Rowlandson*, 1933, no.93;
Reading, Museum and Art Gallery, *Thomas Rowlandson: Drawings from Town and Country*, 1926, no.64;
London, Richard Green & Frank T. Sabin, *Thomas Rowlandson*, 1980, no.2;
London, Leger Galleries, *English Watercolours*, 1984, no.37;
New York, The Frick Collection; Pittsburgh, The Frick Art Museum & Baltimore, Baltimore Museum of Art, *The Art of Thomas Rowlandson*, 1990, no.16;
London, Lowell Libson Ltd, *Beauty and the Beast: A loan exhibition of Rowlandson's works from British private collections*, 2007, no.31.

This masterly and important autobiographical drawing was made by Rowlandson in the 1780s, when he made a number of trips with his friend and sketching companion Henry Wigstead. The marvelously fluid and assured sheet shows the interior of a coach booking office early in the morning with Wigstead and Rowlandson negotiating a journey with the booking clerk. Preserved in exceptional condition, this sheet demonstrates Rowlandson's remarkable facility as a draughtsman and exceptional ability at recording the incidental moments of eighteenth-century life.

Rowlandson and Wigstead are recorded as making three tours together: to the Isle of Wight in 1784, the Brighton in 1789, and to Wales in 1797. The drawings associated with the first are chiefly in the Huntington and, as Robert Wark points out, are from a sketchbook with leaves much smaller in size

than the present sheet.[1] The Welsh drawings are also smaller in size, suggesting that the present sheet relates to the trip to Brighton, although John Hayes has noted that the list of destinations in the coach booking office – 'Coaches Set out from / this Place / Dover / Sandwich / Margate' – points to a Continental trip.[2] Although the internal evidence of the drawing itself raises an alternative possibility. The yawning postilion is seen entering from the right and a porter on the left is seen carrying a large trunk and selection of game, suggesting that the drawing was made at the end of a successful trip to the country. Certainly the page seems to have come from one of Rowlandson's sketchbooks and the verso contains a fascinating colour trial.

Rowlandson regularly commemorated his trips with anecdotal studies of this kind, but rarely are they as exquisitely or beautifully finished as *The Coach Booking Office*. The present drawing was in the collections of the Earl of Mayo, Desmond Coke and Leonard Dent, three of the most distinguished collectors of drawings by Rowlandson.

NOTES
1 R. R. Wark, *Rowlandson's Drawings for a Tour in a Post Chaise*, 1963, San Marino, p.13 note.
2 John Hayes, *The Art of Thomas Rowlandson*, Alexandria, 1990, p.58.

The verso of the drawing showing Rowlandson's characteristic colour trials.

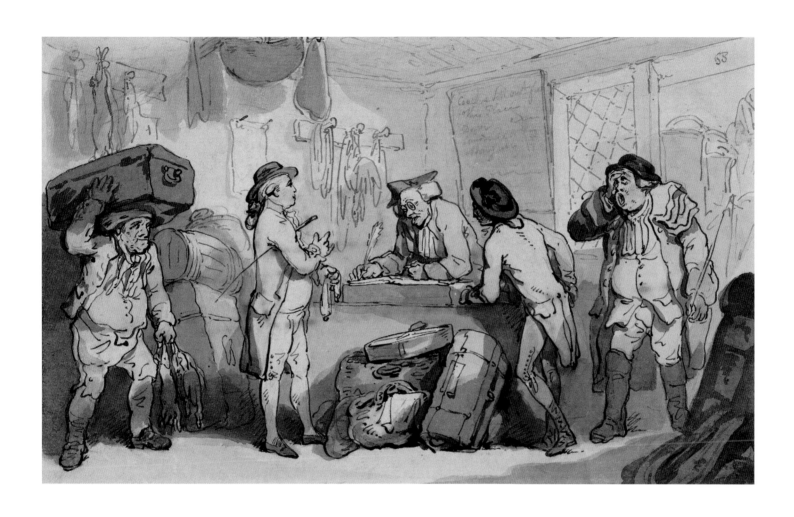

THOMAS GAINSBOROUGH RA 1727–1788

Admiral Thomas Graves

Oil on canvas
50 × 40 inches · 1270 × 1016 mm
Inscribed on a letter on the table:
Rear Admiral Graves / Plymo ... Admiralty
Painted 1785

COLLECTIONS
Admiral Thomas Graves (1725–1802);
Thomas, Lord Graves (1775–1830),
son of the above;
Clarence, 4th Lord Graves (1847–1904),
grandson of the above, to 1896;
Thomas Agnew & Son;
Bought from the above by Wallis;
Sir Joseph B. Robinson, 1st Bart. (1840–1929);
Robinson sale, Christie's, 6 July 1923, lot 6,
re-purchased by the vendor;
Ida Louisa Robinson, Princess Labia
(d.1961), daughter of the above;
Count Natale A.D. Labia,
son of the above, to 1988;
Labia sale, Sotheby's, London,
16 November 1988, lot 60;
A. Alfred Taubman, acquired 1988;
By descent to 2016.

LITERATURE
The Morning Herald, 11 August 1785;
The Morning Herald, 30 December 1786;
Sir Walter Armstrong, *Gainsborough and his
Place in English Art*, London, 1898, p.196;
Sir Walter Armstrong, *Gainsborough and his
Place in English Art*, New York, 1904, p.268;
William T. Whitley, *Thomas Gainsborough*,
London, 1915, pp.244–5 and 257;
R.R.T. 'The Robinson Pictures at Christie's',
The Burlington Magazine, vol. XLIII, July–
December, 1923, p.34;
Ellis K. Waterhouse, 'A Preliminary check
list of portraits by Thomas Gainsborough',
Walpole Society, 1948–1950, vol.XXXIII, p.51;
Ellis K. Waterhouse, *Gainsborough*, 1958 p.71,
no.324.
This painting will be included in the forth-
coming catalogue raisonné of the portraits
of Thomas Gainsborough by Hugh Belsey.

EXHIBITED
London, Schomberg House, 1786;
London, Royal Academy, *The Robinson
Collection*, 1958, no.28
(reproduced in the Souvenir, p.53);
Cape Town, National Gallery of South
Africa, *The Joseph Robinson Collection*,
1959 (70);
Zurich, Kunsthaus, *Sammlung Sir Joseph
Robinson 1840–1929, Werke europäischer Malerei
vom 15. bis 19. Jahrhundert*, 1962, no.56.

This splendid, half-length portrait, was painted by Thomas Gainsborough in 1785 and exhibited to great acclaim in the artist's annual exhibition at Schomberg House the following year. The sitter, Thomas Graves, was a major figure in the naval conflicts of the 1780s and 1790s; he commanded the British force at the Battle of Chesapeake in 1781, the failed action which indirectly led to General Cornwallis's surrender at Yorktown and the loss of America. Painted after the conclusion of the American Revolutionary War and shortly before Graves was to distinguish himself under Lord Howe during the Battle of the 1st June, the portrait can be seen as an important public statement of Graves's position following sustained attacks by his subordinate, Samuel Hood, following the Battle of Chesapeake. The contemporary press accounts of the portrait, principally Henry Bate writing in the Morning Herald, suggest that Gainsborough was conscious of Graves's campaign to clear his name. Made at the height of Gainsborough's powers, Admiral Thomas Graves is a remarkably fluid depiction of a man of action and a quintessential example of Gainsborough's grand manner portraiture.

Thomas Graves was a conventional career sailor. He fought in the Seven Year's War before being made commander-in-chief of the North American squadron in 1781 at the height of the American Revolutionary War. In the summer of that year Cornwallis established his position at Yorktown, Virginia; this in effect made control of the Chesapeake Bay strategically vital. Graves, based in New York, missed news that a French force under Admiral de Grasse had sailed from the Caribbean and taken up position in the bay. Reinforced by a small force under the command of Samuel Hood, Graves sailed for the coast of Virginia with 19 ships of the line. On the morning of 5 September, 1781, the British fleet sighted the French fleet at anchor inside the mouth of the bay.

De Grasse moved quickly to put his ships to sea, where he could maneuver against the British. In their haste, the twenty-four French ships rounded Cape Henry in an undisciplined mass and failed to form a proper battle line. At this point, the British fleet had the opportunity to attack the vessels as they emerged from the Bay. Instead, Graves stopped to form a line of battle, which allowed the French to prepare for the coming action.[1]

The battle was ultimately, indecisive, although, with a significantly smaller force, Graves managed to inflict some damage on the French. During the battle, despite consistently signaling the rear division, commanded by Hood, to engage, it did not come into effective range of the French. For the next two days the rival fleets manoeuvred within sight of each other, but no further engagements took place. The objective for de Grasse was

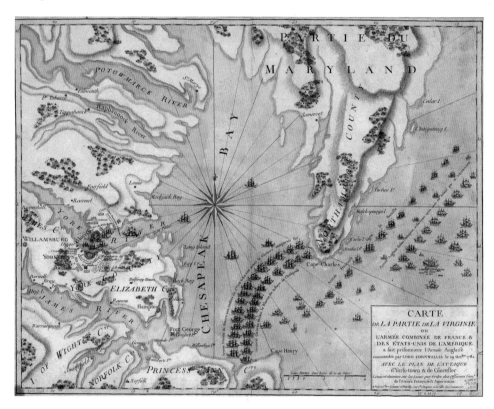

Esnauts et Rapilly, Paris
A plan of the Battle of Chesapeake Bay, 1781
Hand-coloured engraving · 18⅛ × 23⅜ inches · 460 × 590 mm
Library of Congress, Washington, DC

not to destroy the British fleet, but protect the entrance to the Chesapeake Bay. King George III wrote on hearing of the action: 'after knowledge of the defeat of our fleet… I nearly think the empire ruined.' Cornwallis surrendered to General Washington at Yorktown on 19 October, effectively ending the American Revolutionary War.

Before Graves could return to London to defend his actions, Samuel Hood had dispatched a series of letters condemning his conduct and the way the battle had been fought. Hood appeared to have better access to public opinion than Graves. Graves found himself, perhaps unjustifiably, the principal candidate for naval failure and George Germain even proposed he should be court martialled, a course which Lord Sandwich refused to countenance. The reality was that Graves went to the Capes with a force made inadequate by wrong decisions in the West Indies and that in the battle half of Graves's squadron, Hood's division, did not get into action. Graves returned to England in October 1782 in an atmosphere of furious charge and counter-charge for the loss of Yorktown. Public opinion was stirred against him by letters sent by Hood from America and by Admiral Rodney's speeches in the House of Commons.

Thomas Gainsborough's portrait can be read as part of Graves's attempt to clear his name and present himself publicly in the wake of sustained attacks. Graves seems to have gained the support of the Reverend Henry Bate Dudley, the owner and editor of the Morning Herald, who was, in turn a major supporter of Thomas Gainsborough. In August 1785 Bate noted in *The Morning Herald*:

The pencil of Mr Gainsborough has lately been exercised in painting the portrait of Admiral Graves: – an officer of the first professional merit and ability, and a striking contrast to that arrogant naval Lord, whose assured consequence, is founded in idle parade and selfish ostentation.[2]

The 'naval Lord' is presumably a reference to Samuel Hood, who had been made an Irish peer as Baron Hood of Catherington in September 1782 and who continued to issue letters criticising Graves and his conduct. The idea of using a portrait to reaffirm or reinforce public opinion was commonplace by the 1780s. Following a sensational court-martial, Admiral Augustus Keppel was acquitted of charges of insubordination and turned to portraiture as a way of publicising his innocence. His friend, Joshua Reynolds, produced a three-quarter length portrait shortly after the conclusion of the case in 1779.[3] Bate continued his praise of Graves and approbation of Gainsborough's portrait in the pages of the *Morning Herald*:

It is an excellent portrait of that unaffected officer, whose professional merit has suffered somewhat by detraction, but who will long be revered by a body of the navy of the first respect to whom his worth is known.[4]

Graves's portrait was finished by the end of 1785. Gainsborough shows Graves confidently standing in Naval uniform, his hand resting on a letter addressed prominently to: 'Rear Admiral Graves' at Plymouth, underlining the continued confidence he received from his superiors. The billowing red drapery behind Graves himself, his resolute gaze and solid stance all suggest the 'unaffected officer of merit' presented by Bate. The portrait also shows evidence of Gainsborough's continuing interest in Van Dyck. Gainsborough's virtuosic handling of paint in passages such as the gloved hand holding his other glove and the rippling linen on the cuff and stock all point to his appreciation of Van Dyck. Gainsborough has injected in what might be a fairly formulaic portrait of the 1780s a sense of grandeur and virtuosity which he usually reserved for his most important commissions. It is striking that Gainsborough uses the motif of the hand holding the glove in another of his

Thomas Gainsborough RA
Self-portrait, c.1787
Oil on canvas · 30⅜ × 25⅜ inches · 773 × 645 mm
© Royal Academy of Arts, London

most important portraits of the period, the full-length depiction of Charles, 11th Duke of Norfolk at Arundel Castle also painted in 1785.

Gainsborough had fallen out with the Royal Academy in 1784 following their refusal to submit to his somewhat unreasonable hanging instructions. With the support of Bate and the Morning Herald, Gainsborough instead mounted an annual exhibition of his work in his exhibition room at Schomberg House at the same time at the Academy's annual exhibition. Graves's portrait was shown in the 1786 exhibition. It again drew praise from Bate, who noted that:

The portrait of Admiral Graves, a half length, is finished in the best stile; nothing can exceed the colouring.[5]

This is notable praise given the fact that it hung in the company of Gainsborough's full-length portraits of The Duke of Norfolk, Thomas Coke, now at Holkham Hall, and Mrs Richard Brinsley Sheridan now in the National Gallery of Art, Washington. In the review for the exhibition, Bate gave a neat assessment of Gainsborough's late style which encapsulates the portrait of Graves, writing about Lady de Dunstanville, Bate noted that it was:

delicately touched; the most exquisite softness pervades the whole. The hands are finished with the beauty of Vandyke – This picture, from the tenderness of the colouring, should not be hung at a great elevation – its effect will else be diminished.[6]

Shortly after the completion of his portrait, Thomas Graves was promoted vice-admiral of the blue and in 1788 made commander-in-chief at Plymouth. On the outbreak of war with the French in 1793 he was appointed second in command of the Channel Fleet under Lord Howe. He became admiral of the blue and aboard in flagship, the Royal Sovereign, played an important part in the success of the Battle of the 1st of June. He was raised to the Irish peerage as

Baron Graves and awarded a gold medal and chain and a pension of £1,000 per annum.

Gainsborough's depiction of Graves raises questions about the strategies of self-promotion open to painters and sitters in the final decades of the eighteenth century. Gainsborough was famous for his sagacious use of the popular press to promote his work and it is notable that this particular portrait elicited numerous press mentions. More specifically it is notable that those mentions highlight Graves's qualities and recent criticisms, suggesting that Gainsborough, Graves and Bate worked in concert. The portrait itself is a particularly bold example of Gainsborough's late style, the fluid, painterly approach perfectly demonstrates his continued interest in the works of Van Dyck, whilst the careful characterisation underlines his qualities as a

portraitist. Graves's reputation continues to fluctuate and scholars remain divided as to whether he could have been more effective in the face of an overwhelming French force and whether he deserves the epithet: the man who lost America.

NOTES

1 For an authoritative account of the battle see Kenneth Breen, 'Divided command: the West Indies and the North America, 1780–1781', eds. J. Black and P. Woodfine, *The British Navy and the use of naval power in the eighteenth century*, London, 1988, pp.191–206.
2 *The Morning Herald*, 11 August 1785.
3 For Reynolds and Augustus Keppel see David Mannings and Martin Postle, *Sir Joshua Reynolds. A Complete Catalogue of his Paintings*, New Haven and London, 2000, vol.1, p.1048.
4 William T. Whitley *Thomas Gainsborough*, London, 1915, p.244.
5 *The Morning Herald*, 30 December 1786.
6 *The Morning Herald*, 30 December 1786.

Thomas Gainsborough
Charles Howard, 11th Duke of Norfolk, 1784–86
Oil on canvas · 91½ × 60 inches · 2324 mm × 1524 mm
© National Portrait Gallery, London

Gainsborough Dupont,
after Thomas Gainsborough
The Right Honble Lord Rodney KB
Mezzotint · 24⅛ × 15¼ inches · 611 × 389 mm
Published by Benjamin Beale Evans, 1788
© The Trustees of the British Museum

THOMAS ROWLANDSON 1756–1827

Tea on shore

Pen and black ink and watercolour
11½ × 15½ inches · 292 × 393 mm
Drawn *c*.1789

COLLECTIONS
Joseph Grego;
Private collection, UK, *c*.1950 to 1998;
Spink-Leger, London;
Private collection, UK, acquired from
the above 1999, to 2016.

LITERATURE
Joseph Grego, *Rowlandson the Caricaturist*,
1880, pp.168, 253–256, 323;
Royal Institute of Painter's in Water Colour,
The English humorists in art, exhibition
catalogue, London 1889, p.15, repr. p.30;
Lowell Libson, Hugh Belsey, John Basket,
et al, *Beauty and the* Beast: *A loan exhibition of
Rowlandson's works from British private collec-
tions*, 2007, pp.26–7.

EXHIBITED
London, Royal Institute of Painter's in
Water Colour, *The English humorists in art*,
1889, no.107;
London, Lowell Libson Ltd, *Beauty and the
Beast: A loan exhibition of Rowlandson's works
from British private collections*, 2007, no.2.

ENGRAVED
Published by J. Harris as *Tea on Shore*,
January 1789 and reissued with changes
by S. W. Fores in 1794.

This marvelous watercolour is a particularly
impressive example of Rowlandson's large
scale social cartoons. Rowlandson's exquisitely rendered drawing is a masterpiece in
social commentary. Rowlandson paired the
subject, when it was printed, with a composition entitled *Grog on Board*, offering a satire
on the courtship rituals of officers and men.
Preserved in exceptional condition, this
watercolour exemplifies Rowlandson's abilities both as a draughtsman and humourist.

Rowlandson was trained at the Royal
Academy schools, where he unusually
developed as a draughtsman rather than as
a painter. He was not, like so many aspiring
artists, an eager devotee of the president, Sir
Joshua Reynolds, but, following the Hogarth
tradition, responsive to more popular forms
of art, the fashion for drawing caricatures
and the proliferation and profitability of
printselling. A design for publication attributed to Rowlandson dates from 1774, but his
œuvre as a printmaker does not really begin
until 1780, when his works were printed by a
variety of publishers, including Hannah and
W. Humphrey and S. W. Fores. A close friend
of James Gillray, he produced, until the end
of the 1780s, numerous political as well as
social caricatures, though without Gillray's
venom and partisanship.[1] Writing shortly
after the death of Thomas Rowlandson, his
friend, Henry Angelo noted: 'Everyone at
all acquainted with the arts must well know
the caricature works of that very eccentric
genius: the extent of his talent, however, as
a draughtsman is not so generally known…
His powers indeed were so versatile, and his
fancy so rich, that every species of composition flowed from his pen with equal facility.'[2]

The elegant domestic scene depicts two
officers being entertained to tea. To the

left the corpulent, middle aged hostess is being offered a biscuit by a black page, whilst talking to a Naval officer taking snuff; to the right, the daughter of the house is flirting with a young officer, whilst in the center of the composition the head of the household is reduced to filling the teapot from a steaming kettle so engrossed are his wife and daughter in their visitors. The hostess has clearly dressed for the occasion – Rowlandson piles a forest of feathers on her head to suggest an exaggerated adherence to fashion – and is shown in rapt attention at the story of the visiting officer, whilst her daughter, elegantly posed in a picture-hat, is equally fascinated by the young officer. Rowlandson has added Hogarthian touches to amplify the meaning: a pair of caged birds are shown embracing, mirroring the flirtation of the daughter and young officer; a performing dog underlines the status of the black page, exotically – and anachronistically – dressed in a turban.

The composition was published by Rowlandson in 1789 along with its pendant *Grog on Board*. The exceptionally rare first state of the print published in 1784 (one recorded impression in the Royal Collection) shows the woman on the right wearing long tresses and a large hat as seen in our drawing. The re-issue (second state) of 1794 she is shown without a hat and wearing her hair in a shorter style, fashionable in the 1790s. Neither of the two issues of the print show the elaborate picture frame seen in the watercolour. The two scenes offer a perfect contrast of high and low life in port. Whilst *Tea on Shore* shows the officers being entertained and flirting in an elegant interior, *Grog on board* depicts 'Sweet Poll of Plymouth' being entertained below deck. The earthier depiction of life below deck was designed to highlight the similarity between the two arenas – particularly where courting was concerned – and perhaps strip away the artificial formalities of the elegant interior depicted in *Tea on Shore*. The sheet itself is an unusually elegant and beautifully executed watercolour completed by Rowlandson at the height of his powers, the subject matter is handled with unusual subtlety and sophistication and whilst the social commentary is softer than Hogarth the visual puns and ferocious caricature show Rowlandson to be the true inheritor of Hogarth's comic genius.

We are grateful to Nick Knowles for his help in cataloguing this drawing.

NOTES
1 For Rowlandson's prints see Kate Heard, *The Comic Art of Thomas Rowlandson*, exh.cat., London (Royal Collection), 2013, pp.33–50.
2 Henry Angelo, *Reminiscences*, London, 1830, vol.I, p.233.

After Thomas Rowlandson *Tea on Shore*, 1794
Hand-coloured etching with aquatint · 15⅛ × 19½ inches · 385 × 496 mm
Private collection

After Thomas Rowlandson *Grog on Board*, 1789
Hand-coloured etching with aquatint · 16 × 20¼ inches · 409 × 515 mm
Private collection

ARCHIBALD SKIRVING 1749–1819

An elderly woman

Pastels on vellum on the original stretcher
28½ × 23½ inches · 724 × 596mm
Signed and dated, lower right:
A. Skirving 1803
In the original frame

COLLECTIONS
H. W. Cage, 1901;
Esmé Church, d.1972;
Anonymous sale, Clifford Dann & Partners,
Lewes, Sussex, 15–16 April 1980, lot 172;
McEwan Gallery, Ballater;
Edward T. Ash,
(acquired from the above c.1980), 2015;
and by descent, to 2016;
Lowell Libson Ltd
Yale Center for British Art, New Haven,
acquired from the above, 2016.

LITERATURE
H. W. Thompson ed., *The Anecdotes and Egotisms of Henry Mackenzie 1745–1831*, London, 1927, p.213;
Daphne Foskett, *A Dictionary of British Miniature Painters*, 2 vols, London, 1987, pp.236–7, pl.57G, for a discusion of the miniature;
Tanja Sundström, *Aspects of the Life and Work of Archibald Skirving (1749–1819)*, unpublished M.Phil. Thesis, University of St Andrews, 1994;
Stephen Lloyd, *Raeburn's Rival: Archibald Skirving 1749 – 1819*, Scottish National Portrait Gallery, Edinburgh, 1999, pp.67–8, no.99, col. pl.18, (as unknown sitter, possibly Mrs Tait);
Neil Jeffares, *The Dictionary of Pastellists before 1800*, London, 2006, p.502;
Stephen Lloyd and Kim Sloan, *The Intimate Portrait, Drawings, Miniatures and Pastels from Ramsay to Lawrence*, Edinburgh, 2008, p.93, no.49, repr.
Neil Jeffares, *Dictionary of Pastellists before 1800*, online edition.

EXHIBITED
Edinburgh, Scottish National Portrait Gallery, 1999, *Raeburn's Rival: Archibald Skirving 1749w–1819*, no.99;
Edinburgh, Scottish National Portrait Gallery, 2008, *The Intimate Portrait, Drawings, Miniatures and Pastels from Ramsay to Lawrence*, no.49;
On loan to the Scottish National Portrait Gallery, 1999–2016.

This pastel by Archibald Skirving is rightly considered a masterpiece of European portraiture.[1] Drawn in 1803 it is a sensitive and penetrating depiction of old age, rendered with extraordinary fidelity in pastel and, uniquely for the artist, on vellum. Based in Edinburgh for the majority of his career, Skirving's highly finished and technically virtuosic pastel portraits have begun to receive international attention, since the 1999 monographic show at the National Portrait Gallery of Scotland. In their intensity, quality and beauty Skirving's work deserves to be considered in the wider context of European neo-classicism. This pastel is undoubtedly his greatest work and although the sitter is currently unknown, the level of characterisition and 'unflinching realism', to quote Stephen Lloyd, underlines Skirving's place as a major artist of the late eighteenth century.[2]

Archibald Skirving began his career as a junior clerk in the Edinburgh customs office. He is likely to have spent a period at the Trustees' Academy in Edinburgh, where Charles Pavillon was master from 1768 to 1772. In 1777 Skirving moved to London where he had various letters of introduction, including one to John Hamilton Mortimer. He is recorded exhibiting work at the Royal Academy in 1778, where he is described as a miniature painter lodging 'at Mrs Milward's, Little Brook Street, Hanover Square.' But Skirving was unsuccessful in London, returning instead to Scotland. In 1786 he left

for Italy, where in Rome he completed his splendid portrait of the dealer and painter Gavin Hamilton and a self-portrait (both Scottish National Portrait Gallery). His most fruitful period came following his return from Rome in 1795 – and a period of incarceration in Brest for being a spy – when he produced a series of portrait studies of notable Scottish sitters, including the great poet Robert Burns (Scottish National Portrait Gallery).

Skirving was the subject of a biographical essay by Thomas Carlyle, who described his manner of living at the end of his life: 'for perhaps the last 20 or 15 years of his life, he lived in some Flat or Lodging all his own…in complete Hermitage; an indignant but uncomplaining King.' This portrait of Skirving as an introspective and isolated observer neatly mirrors the uncompromising portrayal of his sitters. The writer Henry Mackenzie, who described the artist on one of his visits to Edinburgh, suggests something of the singularity of his working method: 'being the most elaborate and minute of artists made his patients (as they might be called) who were sitting for him sometimes give him fifty or sixty sittings. His portraits were facsimilies, even of the blemishes of the faces which he painted; he never spared a freckle or a smallpox mark.'[3]

This large and highly finished picture neatly reflects Mackenzie's description of Skirving at work. The scrupulous manner in which Skirving has described the sitters features – her lined face, steady stare and sallow cheeks – the attention with which he has described her costume, the mauve dress with a white fichu and a white bonnet dressed with ribbon and tied beneath her chin, along with the fashionable Tamil checked shawl imported from Southern India, all suggest multiple sittings.[4] Whilst Mackenzie's assessment that 'his portraits were facsimilies' underestimates the extraordinary character and emotion present in Skirving's essay on old age. Technically a tour de force, Skirving has used pastel to communicate not only the varying texture of linen, wool and elderly skin, but something of the character of the sitter. The simplicity of the setting and the stark, frontal pose belies the complex mass of pastel marks Skirving used to achieve these effects. The precision of these features testifies to the remarkable condition of the present portrait, which is preserved in its original gilt-wood frame. Whilst this portrait is made by one of Scotland's most important artist, it is in full sympathy with the austere European neo-classicism of the early nineteenth century.

Archibald Skirving
Self-portrait, 1790
Pastel · 28 × 21⅝ inches · 710 × 4550 mm
Scottish National Portrait Gallery, Edinburgh

Archibald Skirving
Lady Pringle, née Emilia Anne Macleod
Pastel
Signed with initials and dated 1815
21¾ × 16 inches · 553 × 407 mm
Yale Center for British Art
(formerly with Lowell Libson Ltd)

NOTES

1 Stephen Lloyd and Kim Sloan, *The Intimate Portrait; Drawings, Miniatures and Pastels from Ramsay to Lawrence*, exh.cat., Edinburgh and London (National Galleries of Scotland and British Museum), p.77.

2 Stephen Lloyd, *Raeburn's Rival: Archibald Skirving 1749 – 1819*, Scottish National Portrait Gallery, Edinburgh, 1999, p.12.

3 Ed. H. W. Thompson, H. Mackenzie, *The Anecdotes and Egotisims of Henry Mackenzie 1745–1831: now first published*, London, 1927, p.212.

4 Stephen Lloyd and Kim Sloan, *The Intimate Portrait; Drawings, Miniatures and Pastels from Ramsay to Lawrence*, exh.cat., Edinburgh and London (National Galleries of Scotland and British Museum), p.77.

RICHARD COSWAY RA 1742–1821

Lavinia, Countess Spencer as Juno

Pencil with touches of watercolour
on laid paper
11½ × 8¼ inches · 290 × 210 mm
Inscribed and dated:
*Richardus Cosway RA FSA et Primarius
Pictor Serenissimi Walliae Principi Fecit
Londini Anno 1806*

Richard Cosway *A woman in classical costume*
from a sketchbook of 119 drawings on 117 leaves,
1765–*c*.1815
Pencil and grey wash
8¾ × 6⅞ inches · 225 × 175 mm
© The Trustees of the British Museum

The sensitively handled drawing demonstrates Cosway's ability to miniaturise the grandeur of contemporary allegorical portraiture. Richard Cosway and his artist wife, Maria, operated both professionally and socially at the highest reaches of society and the subject of this finely drawn portrait, Lavinia, Countess Spencer, was entirely typical of Cosways clients: she was born Lavinia Bingham, daughter of Charles Bingham, 1st Earl of Lucan and in 1781 she married George Spencer, 2nd Earl Spencer, and was painted on a number of occasions by Joshua Reynolds. Lavinia Spencer was a talented amateur draftswoman and printmaker and a number of her drawings were published as prints. Cosway made a drawing of the Countess Spencer reading which she herself etched and published. The drawing itself is a particularly fine example of Cosway's full-length 'stained' or 'tinted' drawings which he produced towards the end of the century, alongside his more prolific output of miniatures. These drawings, in which the faces were painted in detail with watercolour, with the rest of the figure of the composition outlined in graphite. The present drawing is preserved on Cosway's own, wash-lined mount and inscribed with his long Latin signature: *Primarius pictor serenissimi Walliae principis* ('Principal painter to his Royal Highness the Prince of Wales') a form of signiature that he adopted after he was appointed to the post by the Prince of Wales in 1785.[1] More unusual is the iconography.

The Countess Spencer is shown standing in the guise of the goddess Juno receiving the cestus or girdle of Venus from Cupid. The girdle itself bestowed beauty or grace on the wearer; perhaps a curious conceit for the portrait of a woman in her mid-forties who had given birth to nine children by this date. As an iconographical conceit it was not entirely unheard of; Joshua Reynolds had painted an ambitious, full-length portrait of *Lady Blake as Juno* in 1769, showing the sitter standing with a peacock at her side, receiving the girdle from Venus.[2] Cosway made a study for the iconography of the present portrait in a sketchbook preserved in the British Museum.[3] The sketchbook suggests that Cosway worked out possible allegorical guises which would be appropriate for his 'Grand Manner' portraiture which he could then show to prospective sitters.

NOTES

1   See Stephen Lloyd and Kim Sloan, *The Intimate Portrait: Drawings, Miniatures and Pastels from Ramsay to Lawrence*, exh.cat., Edinburgh (National Galleries of Scotland), 2008, p.183.

2   David Mannings and Martin Postle, *Sir Joshua Reynolds: A Complete Catalogue of his Paintings*, New Haven and London, 2000, I, cat.no.186, pp.91–92.

3   London, British Museum 1941,0208.191–307

Richardus Cosway R.A.F.S.Art Primarius Pictor Serenissimi Walliæ Principi. Fecit. Londini Anno 1800

JOHN DOWNMAN RA 1750–1824

Lady Nugent

Pencil, stump and watercolour,
heightened with touches of white
22¼ × 16⅝ inches · 565 × 422 mm
Signed and dated, lower right:
J Downman/ 1810

COLLECTIONS
With Ellis Smith, London;
Private collection, to 2015.

LITERATURE
G.C. Williamson, *John Downman ARA,
His Life and Works,* p.lviii no's. 2 and 3, p.xxxi.

EXHIBITED
London, The Royal Academy, 1810, no.446.

Richard James Lane, after Sir Thomas Lawrence
The Rt Honble Lady Nugent, 1830
Lithograph · 7¾ × 6¼ inches · 198 × 159 mm
© The Trustees of the British Museum

This grand and refined portrait depicts Anne Poulett, the wife of the prominent Whig politician, George Nugent Grenville, later 2nd Baron Nugent. Drawn by Downman at the end of his career and exhibited at the Royal Academy in 1810, this portrait perfectly encapsulates Downman's elegant style of portraiture.

John Downman was born in Ruabon, North Wales, in 1750 and moved to London to become an artist in 1769, training with Benjamin West and enrolling as one of the first students at the newly formed Royal Academy Schools. After a Grand Tour to Italy, where he travelled with Joseph Wright of Derby, Downman returned to London in 1776 and established a practice as a portraitist: first in Cambridge, then in London and the West Country, to which he returned periodically over the next thirty years. Within a few years of his return to London in 1779, he gained a reputation as one of the most fashionable portraitists of the day, and was patronised by the royal family, as well as such fashion icons as the Duchess of Devonshire, the Duchess of Richmond, and Mrs Siddons. His popularity was largely dependent on his ability to work quickly and in quantity. In order to do so he gave up portraits in oil and devised a technique of working in chalks on a lightweight wove paper that allowed him to reproduce up to ten or twelve versions of the same portrait.[1] Downman exhibited 148 works at the Royal Academy between 1770 and 1819; he became an associate of the Royal Academy in 1795, but never gained full membership. His reputation as snobbish, undemocratic, and slow-witted may have lost him the essential support of his peers. In the 1790s his critical popularity began to flag, and towards the

end of that decade he developed a style of chalk portraiture which was larger in scale, bolder in execution, and more penetrating in the description of personality.

This large portrait of Lady Nugent neatly encapsulates Downman's bolder, later, approach to his subjects. Anne Poulett was the second daughter of General the Hon. Vere Pullett, a successful soldier and politician who had been elected MP for Bridgewater in 1790. Anne married her childhood sweetheart George Nugent Greville. Greville was the younger son of George Nugent-Temple, 1st Marquess of Buckingham, whose father was the Prime Minister, George Greville. George Nugent Greville was a Whig politician and author. In 1812 he published *Portugal, a Poem* and in 1829 *Oxford and Locke,* which defended the expulsion of Locke from the University of Oxford against the censures of Dugald Stewart. Downman depicts Lady Nugent seated with a musical score in her lap. An elegant, classical lyre is placed on the column to the right of the composition. The subtle colouring – Lady Nugent's blue shawl, the gilded chair and ornamentation of the lyre and Lady Nugent's features – contrast with the monochrome effect of the rest of the portrait.

NOTE
1 Jane Munro, *John Downman 1750–1824,* exh.cat., Cambridge (Fitzwilliam Museum), 1996, p.13.

JOHN SELL COTMAN 1782–1842

Norwich Cathedral: the north aisle of the choir

Pencil and watercolour
14⅛ × 10¼ inches · 362 × 273 mm
Drawn *c.*1807

COLLECTIONS
Purchased from the artist by his pupil the
Revd James Bulwer (1794–1879);
Bulwer family, by descent, until 1926;
With Walker's Galleries 1926;
C. Morland Agnew (1855–1931);
With Thomas Agnew & Sons by 1936;
A. T. Loyd, Lockinge House, Wantage,
acquired from the above, March 1936;
Christopher 'Larch' Loyd, to 2007;
W/S Fine Art Ltd, London, 2007;
Private collection, UK, acquired from the
above in 2007, to 2016.

LITERATURE
C. F. Bell, 'John Sell Cotman (The Bulwer
Collection)', *Walker's Quarterly*, nos.19–20,
1926, cat.no.9, p.22 and colour plate II;
Francis Russell, *The Loyd Collection of
Paintings, Drawings and Sculpture*, 1990,
revised edition, no.77, p.34 and plate 62;

EXHIBITED
Norwich Art Circle, *John Sell Cotman*,
1888, cat.no.20;
London, Burlington Fine Arts Club,
John Sell Cotman, 1888, cat.no.29;
London, Walker's Galleries, *John Sell Cotman*,
1926, cat.no.9;
London, Agnew's, *Water-Colour and Pencil
Drawings*, 1936, cat.no.129;
London, W/S Fine Art, *Landscape on Paper*,
2007, cat.no.22.

This spare, highly evocative watercolour
was made by John Sell Cotman at the beginning of his career, shortly after he returned
to his native Norwich from a period in
London. Regarded as one of the most
fertile and creative moments in Cotman's
career, his early Norwich watercolours
show a technical innovation and clarity of
vision that has long seen him regarded as
one of the pioneers of the medium and the
true successor to Girtin and his Romanic
vision. In the present sheet, Cotman has
focused on a quiet corner of Norwich
Cathedral, unremarkable from both an
architectural and antiquarian point of view,
building the composition with controlled,
planar washes to create a composition

John Sell Cotman
*The Jesus Chapel, Norwich Cathedral, c.*1807
Pencil and watercolour
15¼ × 10¾ inches · 388 × 272 mm
The Higgins Art Gallery & Museum, Bedford

John Sell Cotman
*The Nave of Norwich Cathedral, c.*1807
Pencil and watercolour
13 × 8¾ inches · 331 × 221 mm
The Higgins Art Gallery & Museum, Bedford

John Sell Cotman
*Screen, Norwich Cathedral, c.*1807
Pencil and watercolour
14 × 10⅝ inches · 359 × 271 mm
©The Trustees of the British Museum

of bold monumentality. It was these flat areas of wash which caused Cotman to be co-opted in the twentieth century as a proto-modernist, as the writer and critic Laurence Binyon noted in his survey *English Water-Colours*, published in 1933: 'there was no need to invoke Cézanne, for Cotman was there to show the way.'[1]

In 1806 Cotman had failed to be elected a member of the newly founded Society of Painters in Water Colours (later known as the Old Watercolour Society) and it was this failure which almost certainly precipitated his return to Norwich. He exhibited for the last time at the Royal Academy and set up a school of drawing in Wymer Street, Norwich. Possibly in a concerted effort to establish himself with the Norwich public, he began to devote himself to the depiction of Norwich architecture. In the 1807 exhibition of the Norwich Society of Artists, founded in 1805 by John Crome and others, Cotman showed twenty works, including three of the city itself. In 1808, his tally rose to 67, but, though he was at pains to demonstrate the full range of his abilities, there were no watercolours of Norwich.

Kitson estimated that there were 'at least ten' drawings of the interior of Norwich cathedral of which the present sheet is one of the most compelling.[2] Cotman's reductive approach means that the composition essentially comprises several powerful geometric shapes created by the carefully modulated washes suggestive of light and shade. By breaking up the washes of greys, browns and ochres and leaving small irregular patches of paper exposed, the Cotman suggests the textures of worn stone and wood. The precise purpose of the watercolours of Norwich Cathedral

are not clear. There is no indication that he intended to publish them; most, such as the present sheet, show minor features of the cathedral and would have served little antiquarian purpose. Andrew Hemingway has suggested that Cotman's choice of views suggest a considerable interest in pre-gothic architecture, 'which was felt to express the sobriety and virility of Norman culture.'[3] The scarred wall shows the evidence of funerary brasses having been removed and the box pews have been inexpertly built into the remains of an earlier tomb suggesting that Cotman might have been alive to debates around desecration following the Reformation.[4] But the present view seems more likely to represent a picturesque interest in dilapidation which characterises much of Cotman's work at this moment. Other views from the series show corners of Norwich Cathedral that had been largely forgotten, for example the impressive sheet depicting *Jesus Chapel* now in the Cecil Higgins Art Gallery, Bedford, shows the space being used as a lumber room, with a ladder propped up against the wall.

The watercolour is in exceptional condition and has an unbroken provenance, having originally belonged to the Revd. James Bulwer, Cotman's pupil. The Bulwer collection was described as 'nearly as rich as that of Dawson Turner in antiquarian material' and 'immeasurably more so in artistic quality.'[5] At least three watercolours from this series were in Bulwer's collection including two sheets now in the Cecil Higgins Art Gallery.[6] It was then owned by Charles Morland Agnew, a partner in Agnew's, who formed an outstanding collection of early English watercolours. After his death it was acquired by A.T. Loyd for the important

collection of old master and British works at Lockinge House in Oxfordshire.

Whilst Cotman's contemporaries were equivocal about his art, he had been lionised by later painters. Paul Nash, Eric Ravilious and John Piper celebrated Cotman in their search for a recognisably British tradition that could be reconciled with developments in modern European painting. The economy, clarity and reductive forms present in *Norwich Cathedral: the North Aisle of the Choir* perfectly demonstrate why Cotman's early watercolours had this appeal.

NOTES

1 Laurence Binyon, *English Watercolours*, London, 1933, p.191.

2 Sydney D. Kitson, *The Life of John Sell Cotman*, 1982, p.107.

3 Andrew Hemingway, 'Meaning in Cotman's Norfolk subjects', *Art History*, vol.7 no.1, March 1984, p.71.

4 Evelyn Joll, *Cecil Higgins Art Gallery: Watercolours and Drawings*, 2002, pp.69, 71; Miklos Rajnai et al, *John Sell Cotman 1782–1842*, exh cat., London (Victoria and Albert Museum), 1982, no.62, pp.91–93, no.65, pp.93–95.

5 C. F. Bell, 'John Sell Cotman (The Bulwer Collection)', *Walker's Quarterly*, nos 19–20, 1926 p.5.

6 Evelyn Joll, *Cecil Higgins Art Gallery: Watercolours and Drawings*, 2002, pp.69, 71; Miklos Rajnai et al, *John Sell Cotman 1782–1842*, exhibition catalogue, V&A and elsewhere, 1982, no.62, pp.91–93, no.65, pp.93–95. The Higgins Art Gallery & Museum's drawings are C. F. Bell's nos 6 (*Jesus Chapel*) and 8 (*Interior of the Nave*) pp.21, 22.

JOHN CONSTABLE RA 1776–1837

Approaching night: a coastal scene at dusk

Oil on paper laid down on canvas
6 × 9¾ inches · 152 × 248 mm
Painted in the early 1820s

COLLECTIONS
John Constable RA;
Hugh Constable, grandson of the artist, by descent;
Sir Michael Sadler (1861–1943);
Michael Sadler, son of the above;
Mrs Michael Sadler, wife of the above to 1960;
Sadler sale, Christie's, 18 November 1960, lot 88, purchased by Tischaff;
Private collection, USA, to 2003;
Lowell Libson Ltd;
Private collection, UK, purchased from the above 2004, to 2016.

EXHIBITED
London, Burlington Fine Arts Club, 1934, no.18 (lent by Sir Michael Sadler);
London, Wildenstein, *Centenary Exhibition: John Constable RA: His origins and influence*, May 1937, no.32 (lent by Sir Michael Sadler);
London, Guildhall Art Gallery, *John Constable Exhibition*, 1952, no.4 (lent by Michael Sadler).

The present study is a rare example of Constable working *en plein air* in the evening and as such provides an important counterpoint to his daytime sky and coast studies. Executed in fluid, rapidly applied oil, the atmospheric study demonstrates Constable's extraordinary ability at capturing effects of light and climate. This boldly executed oil study was made in the early 1820s at the moment Constable was developing his distinctive and revolutionary approach to capturing weather effects and shifting light.

It was during his residence in Hampstead that the sky became the most crucial determinant of the character of his landscape painting.[1] Writing to his friend and correspondent, John Fisher, from Hampstead in October 1821 Constable noted:
If the sky is obtrusive – (as mine are) it is bad, but if they are evaded (as mine are not) it is worse… It will be difficult to name a class of Landscape, in which the sky is not the 'key note', the standard of Scale, and chief 'Organ of Sentiment'… The sky is the 'source of Light' in nature – and governs every thing.'[2]

As a 'chief Organ of Sentiment' Constable's sky studies have long been recognised as congruent with the emerging Romantic ideas expressed in poetry. Michael Rosenthal highlighted an analogous response in the work of William Wordsworth.[3] In 1821 Constable wrote to John Fisher on his responsiveness to rain and stormy weather in particular: 'I have likewise made many *skies* and effects – for I wish it could be said of me as Fuselli says of Rembrandt, "he followed nature in her calmest abodes and could pluck a flower on every hedge – yet he was born to cast a steadfast eye on the bolder phenomena of nature". We have had noble clouds & effects of light & dark

& colour.'[4] Constable was particularly susceptible to grand sunsets and the liminal moments of the day, although nocturnal views are rare.

Graham Reynolds, in a letter of 8th March 2003, confirmed the attribution to Constable and further suggested that the subject could be an estuary near Maningtree or Mistley in Suffolk and tentatively dates the picture to circa 1820. Anne Lyles has also pointed out the similarity in the handling of the paint to certain coastal as well as sea and sky studies of the early 1820s made in the Brighton area. Constable was evidently having to work very rapidly to capture the fast changing point at which dusk turns to night and to that end appears to have deliberately employed very heavily thinned oils, handling them much as one would watercolours: the unusual heavily textured paper compensating for the impasto which would normally be found in similar studies made during the day.

Using thinned paint and a monochrome palette of white and black, Constable has cleverly evoked the expansiveness of sky over sea. The restricted palette also evokes the sense of the gloaming scene, as sky and sea converge. This abbreviated style typifies Constable's most atmospheric *plein air* sky studies of the 1820s. The present, informal sketch passed from Constable to his grandson, Hugh and was then acquired by the great educationalist and collector, Sir Michael Sadler.

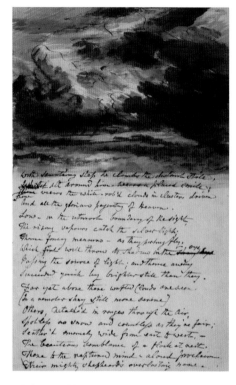

John Constable
Cloud Study with verses from Bloomfield
Ink on paper watermarked 1817
13⅝ ×8¾ inches · 335×211 mm
© Tate, London 2017

NOTES

1   R. B. Beckett, *John Constable's Correspondence*, Suffolk, 1968, vol.vi, 1968, p.228.
2   R.B. Beckett, *John Constable's Correspondence*, Suffolk, 1968, vol.vi, pp.76–77.
3   Michael Rosenthal, *Constable: The Painter and his Landscape*, New Haven and London, 1983, p.167.
4   R. B. Beckett, *John Constable's Correspondence*, Suffolk, 1968, vol.vi, 1968, p.74.

With saunt'ring step he climbs the distant stile,
Whilst all around him wears a placid smile;
There views the white-rob'd clouds in clusters driven
And all the glorious pageantry of Heaven.
Low – on the utmost boundary of the sight,
The rising vapours catch the silver light;
Thence fancy measurs – as they parting fly,
Which first will throw its shadow on the eye
Passing the source of light; and thence away
Succeeded quick by brighter still than they.
Far yet above these wafted Clouds are seen
(In a remoter sky still more serene)
Others, detach'd in ranges through the Air,
Spotless as snow and countless as they're fair;
Scatter'd imensely wide from east to west, –
The beauteous semblance of a flock at rest.
These to the raptured mind – aloud proclaim
Their mighty shepheard's everlasting name.

ROBERT BLOOMFIELD,
Winter from *The Farmer's Boy*

SAMUEL PALMER 1805–1881

Mountainous landscape, Wales

Watercolour and gouache over pencil
4⅞ × 6¾ inches · 125 × 170 mm
Drawn c.1834

COLLECTIONS
Private collection, UK, to 2016.

In the 1830s, following his years in Shoreham, Samuel Palmer visited Devon, Somerset and North Wales in his quest for evocative landscapes. In October of 1834 Palmer wrote enthusiastically to his friend, the painter George Richmond that he felt 'more energetic and ambition for excellence in art than ever.'[1] In the following two summers he explored the mountains, castles and wilderness of Wales, which were to fire his imagination, before he set off to Italy in 1837. This beautifully executed, compact watercolour shows an extensive view across a Welsh valley. Executed in pencil and rapid, fluid washes the drawing contains many of the pictorial devices which were central to his work in the mid-1830s.

Palmer's landscapes are rarely purely topographical and in this concentrated watercolour study Palmer preserves a sense of his visionary response to place. The steep sides of the Welsh hills, the blue floor of the valley and the arched, abbreviated form of the tree clinging to the slope all recall Palmer's most magical compositions of the mid-1830s, such as *The Golden Valley*. Whilst the cooler palette and rapid mark making point to this sketch having been made on the spot, whilst Palmer was working in Wales.

Palmer's son described his father's general sketching apparatus on these expeditions: *There were no costly umbrellas, elaborate boxes, or well-filled portmanteaus. A narrow deal case, or, at other times, a capacious sketching portfolio, slung round the shoulders with a strap, held a good supply of paper, with two large but very light wooden palettes, set with clots of colour a quarter of an inch thick, upon a coat of enamel formed of flake-white and copal. A light hand-basket held the remainder of the more bulky materials, with the lunch or dinner,*

and a veteran camp-stool which had survived the Italian campaign. A quantity of capacious pockets were filled with sharp knives, chalks, charcoal, crayons, and sketch-books; and a pair of ancient neutral-tint spectacles carried, with a little diminishing mirror, specially for sunsets, completed the equipment.[2]

This charming and highly energized watercolour study evokes in its abbreviations of forms the more abstract of Palmer's works, whilst in its grandeur and scope looks forward to the great exhibition watercolours of the 1840s and 1850s. Probably worked on a page from a sketchbook, this rapid, informal study is a rare survival in Palmer's oeuvre as much of his preparatory work – particularly his preparatory watercolours – were destroyed by his widow and son following his death.[3]

Samuel Palmer *The Weald of Kent*, 1833–4
Watercolour and gouache · 7⅜ × 10⅝ inches · 187 × 270 mm
Yale Center for British Art, Paul Mellon Collection

NOTES
1 Ed. R. Lister, *The Letters of Samuel Palmer*, Oxford 1974, p.64.
2 A. H. Palmer, 'The Story of an Imaginative Painter', *The Portfolio: An Artistic Periodical*, 15, 1884, pp.148–149.
3 William Vaughan, *Samuel Palmer: Shadows on the Wall*, New Haven and London, 2015, pp.366.

SAMUEL PALMER 1805–1881

A Wooded Landscape

Black chalk, watercolour and white
heightening on buff paper
14 × 20¾ inches · 360 × 527 mm
Drawn *c*.1849

COLLECTIONS
The artist;
Alfred Herbert Palmer (1853–1931),
son of the artist;
Walker's Galleries, Bond Street.

LITERATURE
To be included by Colin Harrison in his
revised catalogue raisonné of the works of
Samuel Palmer.

This previously unpublished work is an
unusually large and ambitious drawing
made by Samuel Palmer at a key moment in
his career. Probably made whilst he was stay-
ing in Clovelly in north Devon in 1849, the
complex and richly handled monochrome
sheet shows the way in which Palmer
responded to landscape as his career became
increasingly focused on watercolour painting
and printmaking. The highly sophisticated
exploration of the walk of trees in black
chalk and the articulation of the architecture
of the foliage points to Palmer's continued interest in the close study of nature.
Throughout his career Palmer produced
vivid tree studies, from the great watercolours of oaks in Lullingstone Park, commissioned by John Linnell, to *The Willow*, made
in *c*.1850 which Palmer turned into his first
etching the same year. Drawn with remarkable assurance and filled with characteristic
emotion, this striking sheet is an important
rediscovery and adds to our understanding
of Palmer's development around 1850.

The 1840s saw Palmer as a married man,
desperately attempting to build a successful business as a painter to support his
growing family. Based in London, Palmer
took on a number of paying pupils whilst

focusing his artistic attention on producing
works for exhibition. As William Vaughan
has noted, it was during the 1840s that
Palmer's work took on a new sense of
'drama and simplification', as he tried to
find a commercial mode for his landscape
painting.[1] Palmer had recently been elected
to the Old Watercolour Society (1843) and
was intent on using the forum of the annual
exhibitions to find a formula which would
make his pictures financially successful.
Palmer began to travel widely to collect
material for his Berkshire, Buckinghamshire,
Surrey, Somerset, Devon, Cornwall, the Isle
of Wight, the Lake District, and Wales, he
used on the spot sketches as the basis for his
exhibition works.

In July 1849 Palmer was in Devon and
wrote to an unidentified friend, probably the
painter George Richmond:
Woods and woody hills must be juicy and rich;
real TREE COLOUR, *not anything picture colour.*
Detached, elegant trees sometimes stand out
into the glade; and above the woody or arable
hill-tops, a bit of much higher hill is sometimes
visible, [all] heaving and gently lifting themselves,
as it were, towards the heavens and the sun. It is
of no use to try woody hills without a wonderful
variety of texture based on the modeling.[2]

This letter gives a sense of the intensity with which Palmer assimilated the landscape. Whilst colour is absent from this highly finished monochrome 'watercolour', Palmer has approached it in a characteristic way. Like so much of Palmer's work, the drawing, whilst elaborate and richly worked in parts, conceals none of its stages of development. It shows the bold 'first lines' that mapped out the whole composition – the spidery black chalk marks which delineate the branches and give the underlying structure to the trees. Over this framework Palmer has built up washes of watercolour and over this applied touches of white gouache to give the sense of light filtering through the canopy. The focus of the composition is the masterfully handled clump of trees to the left and the path glimpsed through the wood, the bank to the right and screen of trees are barely suggested, preserving this drawing's sketch-like quality. At about the same date as this drawing, Palmer made a similar study of a *Willow* now in Manchester City Gallery, it was published by Palmer as an etching in 1850, suggesting that the present work, with its suggestive concealed path may also have been intended as a subject for one of his early etchings.

This boldly worked and exceptionally well preserved drawing passed from Samuel Palmer to his son A. H. Palmer, it was sold by Walker's Galleries in Bond Street in the 1940s and is published here for the first time.

Samuel Palmer
Oak Tree and Beech, Lullingstone Park, 1828
Pen and brown ink, pencil and watercolour
11⅝ × 18½ inches · 296 × 470 mm
Thaw Collection. The Morgan Library & Museum, 2006.53

Samuel Palmer
A Woodland Study, c.1856
Brush and black and brown washes, heightened with white and scratching-out on 'London' board
8⅞ × 6¾ inches · 225 × 172 mm
The Art Institute of Chicago, gift of Dorothy Braude Edinburg to the Harry B. and Bessie K. Braude Memorial Collection (formerly with Lowell Libson Ltd)

Samuel Palmer
The Willow, 1850
Etching and drypoint · 4⅝ × 3¼ inches · 118 × 82 mm
The Yale Center for British Art, Yale Art Gallery Collection, The G. Allen Smith Collection

NOTES

1 William Vaughan, *Samuel Palmer: Shadows on the Wall*, New Haven and London, 2015, p.274.
2 Ed. Raymond Lister, *The Letters of Samuel Palmer*, Oxford, 1974, 1, p.473.

JOHN MARTIN 1789–1854
The City of God

Oil on canvas
18 × 26 inches · 460 × 660 mm
Painted *c.*1850–51

And I heard a great voice out of heaven saying,
Behold, the tabernacle of God is with men…
And the city had no need of the sun, neither of
the moon, to shine in it: for the glory of God did
lighten it, and the Lamb is the light thereof.

The Book of Revelation, XXI: 2 & 23.

This exceptionally rare painting was made by Martin towards the end of his career *c.*1850, whilst he was working on his most important series of paintings depicting *The Last Judgment, Great Day of his Wrath* and *Plains of Heaven* all now in the Tate. *The City of God* can be viewed as partly a preliminary to Martin's major pictorial enterprise, but also as a stand-alone work in which he explored the pictorial effects and potential of the subject of heaven as described in the Book of Revelation. In the design of *The City of God* Martin brings together many of the compositional motifs – rocky outcrop, heavenly architecture, spectacular lighting effects and distant landscape – which had preoccupied him throughout his career. Preserved in outstanding condition, Martin's canvas offers important evidence of his working practice whilst he was in the midst of executing his three most important paintings.

Martin was born in Northumberland and began his career apprenticed initially to a coach-painter in Newcastle upon Tyne and then to the china painter, Boniface Musso, whom he accompanied to London in 1805. He first exhibited at the Royal Academy in 1811, but first made an impact the following year with *Sadak in Search of the Waters of Oblivion* (St Louis Art Museum, Missouri), a painting remarkable for its combination of dramatic composition and luminous colouration that was to be Martin's speciality for the rest of his career. Martin then produced a series of successful paintings including *The Bard, The Fall of Babylon*, exhibited in 1819 at the British Institution and *Belshazzar's Feast* for which Martin won a £200 premium at the Royal Academy exhibition of 1821. Martin

emerged as an artist who was capable of using compositional effects, subject-matter and publicity to appeal to a mass audience. *Belshazzar's Feast* was acquired by the glass painter William Collins, who, in partnership with Martin, exhibited the painting in his shop on The Strand before it toured the country.[1] A description published to accompany the painting sited the archaeological accuracy of Martin's use of architecture; Martin the showman recognized the allure of 'authenticity' while relying on the pull of crude perspectives. As the German critic G. F. Waagen said, such paintings as *Belshazzar* 'unite in a high degree the qualities which the English require above all in a work of art—effect, a powerful invention, and topographical historical truth.'[2] Martin achieved great commercial success and an international reputation through the prints of his works. Martin's conscious popularism meant that he was never fully accepted by the artistic establishment and never became a member of the Royal Academy.

After financially unsuccessful attempts at developing engineering and urban schemes and attempting to bring about reform of the copyright laws, Martin was facing financial ruin. He retrenched and began producing landscape watercolours, returning in the 1850s to the monumental panoramas of Miltonic and biblical subjects with which he had found his fame. In around 1845 Martin began to work on the *Last Judgement* triptych, the monumental works which were to become his lasting testament. The colossal paintings re-established Martin's reputation, they toured internationally, were turned into popular engravings and were critically acclaimed. *The City of God*

can be viewed as an early part of Martin's painting campaign on the three great canvases; our painting relates specifically to the composition of the third of his *Last Judgment* triptych, *The Plains of Heaven*.

Michael Campbell has pointed out that *The City of God* shows Martin using many of the compositional motifs he had developed throughout his working career. Martin created a characteristically epic celestial landscape; lush, exotic trees are silhouetted against a meandering river, a range of hills are framed against purple mountains and the distant landscape dissolves into a pink horizon which merges with the sky. The rocky outcrop partially obscuring a fantastical city was a characteristic trope which Martin used in his earliest works, such as his 1816 painting *Joshua Commanding the Sun to Stand Still Upon Gibeon*. The two figures standing on the outcrop, one with arm outstretched, silhouetted against the celestial light are

characteristic of Martin's work throughout his life. So too are the ornate barges, placidly floating on the waters, which first appear in Martin's work in the late 1820s and become more and more elaborate on each occasion. The prows of the barges are almost identical to that of the ship in which Jesus is seen commanding the waters in *Christ Stilleth the Tempest* of 1852 (York City Art Gallery) and the boats which dominate the foreground of the *Destruction of Tyre* (Toledo Museum of Art) painted in 1840. This composite method reflects Martin's own recorded working practice. A remarkable album survives in the V&A in which Martin selected favourite compositional elements from the prints made after his paintings, cutting them up and pasting them to act as an aid for the creation of new compositions, underlining that Martin thought of his pictures in terms of their separate parts.[3]

When this painting was rediscovered in the 1980s the Martin scholar William Feaver incorrectly identified the subject as *The Celestial City and the River of Bliss*, a painting which had been exhibited at the Royal Academy in 1841. But as Michael Campbell has argued the subject is not from Milton or Bunyan, but the Bible and forms part of Martin's general exploration of the Book

of Revelation which culminates in the *Last Judgment* triptych now in the Tate.

In its palette, handling and composition *The City of God* recalls much of Martin's earlier work, but as Michael Campbell has confirmed: this painting dates to the last decade of his career. The striations in the rocky outcrop are more abbreviated and stylised than those in his earliest paintings, where each strata is frequently delineated, the atmospheric sky is more freely painted and the vegetation is less minutely handled, all hallmarks of his later technique. Campbell has suggested that the present painting may have been left partially unfinished by Martin as the, passage depicting the mountains in the distance on the left appear not to have the characteristic highlights that one might expect. This passage reveals the soft brown ground which is characteristic of Martin. This underlines the composite nature of Martin's working practice whereby he left reserves in place for areas to be worked up at different stages. Campbell has suggested that the foliage on the right hand side of the canvas and foreground details, such as the architectural fragment carved with figures was completed under his supervision by one of Martin's sons, possibly his frequent collaborator, Alfred Martin. The

present painting is not recorded in any of Martin's posthumous sales and it probably was sold during his own lifetime. This may explain why it was never exhibited during Martin's lifetime and was left unsigned unlike the majority of his aggrandising exhibition works.

Martin was a master when working on a grand scale; producing monumental public works, but he was equally adept at distilling his epic ideas into a smaller format. In this beautifully preserved and intensely handled painting, Martin has communicated the epic nature of the Book of Revelation on a cabinet scale. As Michael Campbell has noted: 'few of [Martin's] visionary works of this quality are still available, I view this painting as a work of some significance.'

We are extremely grateful to Michael Campbell for his help in cataloguing this painting.

NOTES
1   Ed. Martin Myrone, *John Martin: Apocalypse*, exh.cat., London (Tate Gallery), 2011, pp.99–108.
2   G. F. Waagen, *Works of Art and Artists in England*, 1838, London, vol.II, p.162.
3   For John Martin's Album see Ed. Martin Myrone, *John Martin: Apocalypse*, exh.cat., London (Tate Gallery), 2011, cat.no. 79, pp.146–147.

John Martin
The Plains of Heaven, 1851–3
Oil on canvas
78¼ × 120¾ inches · 1988 × 3067 mm
© Tate, London 2017

John Martin
Joshua commanding the Sun to stand still, 1827
Mezzotint with etching, on steel plate
22 × 29⅞ inches · 560 × 760 mm
© The Trustees of the British Museum

John Martin
Christ stilleth the Tempest, 1852
Oil on paper on card
20 × 30 inches · 508 × 762 mm
© York Museums Trust (York Art Gallery), UK/Bridgeman Images

JOHN RUSKIN 1819–1900

Thun

Pencil and watercolour heightened
with white on blue wove drawing paper
13¼ × 18½ inches · 336 × 470 mm
Inscribed lower right: *Thun*
Drawn 1854

COLLECTIONS
Private collection, Australia;
Private collection, UK, purchased from the
above 2007, to 2016.

Writing to Pauline, Lady Trevelyan in 1854,
Ruskin noted:
*Out of four months on the Continent, I have
taken only ten days of whole work, and ten days
half work: those were to make some drawings
of old bits of Thun and Fribourg, likely to be
destroyed before I get back to them again.*[1]
The present, characteristic view of Thun
was the result of one of these visits. The
sweeping panorama shows the town from
the east looking west; the turrets of Thun
castle are prominent on the right and the
river Aare is shown meandering off to the
right whilst a straight road – now called
the Allmendstrasse – stretches into the
distant Alps. This watercolour demonstrates
Ruskin's debt to Renaissance landscape
drawings and prints, his elevated position
allowed him to produce a bird's eye' view
of the town, similar to the mountainous
landscape which Dürer included in his
great depiction of *Nemesis*. In this largely
tonal study, Ruskin has produced a near
monochrome work to capture the effect of
light; Ruskin records the light reflecting on
the river with touches of white gouache,
whilst the distant hills are executed in rich
blue watercolour.

In common with other expansive
landscapes Ruskin produced in Switzerland,
his view of Thun includes areas which are

densely delineated and passages which are
entirely bare of detail. It was a method
which Ruskin promoted to his own students
in *The Elements of Drawings*: 'When your
time is short, or the subject is so rich in
detail that you feel you cannot complete it
intelligently in light and shade, make a hasty
study of the effect, and give the rest of the
time to a Düreresque expression of details.'[2]

Ruskin's motivation for executing these
topographical studies in the Alps seem
to have been partly his interest in Turner
– who produced numerous atmospheric
studies of Thun and its lake – and partly
antiquarian. As Ruskin expressed in his
letter to Pauline Trevelyan, he was keen
to capture aspects of the town before they
were destroyed. This explains both the
sensitivity to light and atmosphere manifest
in the composition and the careful attention
to architectural detail. Ruskin produced a
number of expansive landscape drawings of
Swiss towns but this is an unusually sensitive
and fully resolved work. The purpose of
Ruskin's studies were to further define
Turner's view of Switzerland and to distil
his own interest in the inter relationship of
Swiss architecture, history and landscape.
As such the present sheet, with its careful
depiction of Thun Castle, the city walls and
its principal church, the fourteenth-century
Statdkirche and their relationship to the
sinuous river and the distant mountains
makes a neat visual analogy of Ruskin's
aims and aspirations.

NOTES
1 Robert Hewison, *Ruskin, Turner and the Pre-
Raphaelites*, exh.cat., London (Tate), 2000, p.165.
2 Quoted in Paul H Walton, *Master Drawings by
John Ruskin: selections from the David Thomson
collection*, 2000, p.88.

J. M. W. Turner
*Town and Lake of Thun, c.*1838
Watercolour · 8⅞ × 11¼ inches · 227 × 287 mm
The Higgins Art Gallery & Museum, Bedford, UK/Bridgeman Images

J. M. W. Turner
Ville de Thun, Switzerland, 1816
Mezzotint and etching, engraved by Thomas Hodgetts
for *Liber Studiorum*
8⅜ × 11½ inches · 212 × 292 mm
© The Trustees of the British Museum

JOHN RUSKIN 1819–1900

Bellinzona, Switzerland looking north towards the St Gotthard Pass

Pencil, watercolour and gouache
21⅛ × 14½ inches · 538 × 368 mm
Inscribed on an old back label:
*Sketch – John Ruskin. / Given to Rev'd Moore
on his leaving Camberwell 1866 by J. Ruskin.*
Drawn 1858

COLLECTIONS
Margaret Ruskin, the artist's mother;
Rev. Daniel Moore, a gift from the artist and
Margaret Ruskin in 1866;
with Agnew's, London;
Anon. sale; Sotheby's, London,
15 March 1967, lot 23;
Christie's, London, 20 November 2003,
lot 49;
Private collection, UK,
purchased from the above, to 2016.

LITERATURE
E.T. Cook and A.J. Wedderburn, *The Library
Edition of the Works of John Ruskin*, London,
1903–1912, vol.XXXVIII, no.188.

This highly impressive watercolour is
one of the most important compositions
completed by Ruskin on his painting trips to
the Alps during the 1850s. Whilst the view
chosen represented a deliberate homage
to Turner, Ruskin's Bellinzona offers an
important visual departure from Turner's
atmospheric watercolours. Ruskin's palette,
approach to composition and form all point
towards his increasing interest in the world
of the Pre-Raphaelites. The gestation of this
exceptionally well documented sheet was
frequently mentioned in Ruskin's extensive
correspondence and it was a watercolour of
which Ruskin thought exceptionally highly.
Ruskin gave this work to his mother and in
1866 he and his mother presented it to the
Rev Daniel Moore. Ruskin's parents had
first met Moore and his wife in Paris on a
Continental trip in 1851 when the party went
on to tour through Switzerland together.
Ruskin thought he was a 'most agreeable
companion.' The Ruskin family attended the
Camden Chapel where Moore was minister
and this drawing was presented to him on
his retirement.

After crossing the Alps in 1845 Ruskin
was unimpressed with Bellinzona, but he
was subsequently won over by the charm
of the place and in his first selection of a
hundred watercolours from the Turner
Bequest, Ruskin selected, with a view to
demonstrating the value of exhibiting
unfinished sketches, eight views of
Bellinzona. In the accompanying catalogue
he described Bellinzona as 'on the whole
the most picturesque in Switzerland, being
crowned by three fortresses, standing
on isolated rocks of noble form, while
the buildings are full of beautiful Italian
character.'[1]

The Church of San Quirico above Bellinzona
looking north towards the St Gotthard
Photograph courtesy of David Hill

Arriving on 12 June 1858 Ruskin now found Bellinzona 'quite like a wonderful dream.' He remained in the town until the 8 July and it was during this stay that the present drawing was executed. From Bellinzona Ruskin drove to the head of the lake, and took the steamer for Baveno and the Isola Bella, from where on the 8 July Ruskin wrote to his father about the execution of the present drawing:

I went every evening to draw his [the priest's] garden; and where, by the steps cut in its rock, and the winding paths round it, and the vines hanging over it, and the little patch of golden corn at the bottom of it, and the white lily growing on a rock in the midst of it, and the white church tower holding the dark bells over it, and the deep purple mountains encompassing it, I got so frightfully and hopelessly beaten. It was partly the priest's fault too, for he cut down the lily to present to the Madonna one festa day-not knowing that it was just at the heart of my subject-and a day or two afterwards he cut his corn ... which took away all my gold as before he had taken all my silver, and so discouraged me.[2]

As with many of his most important compositions at this date, Ruskin was beset with doubts and the problem of trying to capture the whole experience of the place. He was continually comparing his work unfavourably with that of Turner. In a letter to the painter John Frederick Lewis on 6 August 1858 Ruskin calculated that 'it would take to finish the drawing ... Fifteen years, six months & some days'.[3] This was humorous reiteration of a genuine dilemma, as he explained to his father: ' ... my standard is now too high to admit of my drawing with any comfort, as least unless I gave up everything else for it.'[4]

The vivid watercolour, originally executed on blue paper (now faded), is in fact far from Turner in its touch and approach. The rich palette, architectural structure (heightened by Ruskin's use of a strong vertical composition) and the almost abstract details, such as the pattern of silhouetted leaves, point to Ruskin's visual innovation.

Ruskin considered the composition significant enough to present it first to his mother and then to his friend the Rev. D. Moore. The letter accompanying its gift to the latter explained:

Denmark Hill 22nd Oct 1866
Dear Mr Moore
I have made no drawings at any time but for notes of fact: more for pleasure of sketching – so that I have had great difficulty in finding one that seemed the least fit for presentation to you. Nor can I ever conceive any one taking any pleasure in my imperfect work. However the sketch I send looks pretty well at a distance, and it is of an interesting scene enough, in its way. the little rocky garden & the view of village near Bellinzona – which being much too steep for the old priest to trouble himself by walking – much less working in – had near perished by drought when I sketched it – though a mountain stream dashed by only a hundred yards below. – from which – when I was tired of drawing, my guide & I brought up sundry bucketsfull of snow water to the poor garden – much to its refreshment – and the villagers' astonishment and our own piece of mind – for that afternoon. The valley in the distance is the ascent access to the pass of the St Gothard. – you are looking north.

This sketch belonged to my mother but she likes you to have it. & so do I, if you like it. I wish the fig leaves had stalks to them (or stitches together at any rate), but I got tired at the time of the tailoring and I can't do it now rightly.
Ever affectionately Yours
J Ruskin

J. M. W. Turner *Bellinzona from the road to Locarno: sample study*, 1841
Gouache, pencil and watercolour · 9 × 11⅜ inches · 229 × 289 mm
From the Fribourg, Lausanne and Geneva sketchbook, TB CCCXXXII 25
© Tate, London 2017

NOTES

1   E.T. Cook and A.J. Wedderburn, *The Library Edition of the Works of John Ruskin*, London, 1903–1912, V.XIII, p.207.

2   E.T. Cook and A.J. Wedderburn, *The Library Edition of the Works of John Ruskin*, London, 1903–1912, V.VII, p.xxxvi.

3   Robert Hewison, *Ruskin, Turner and the Pre-Raphaelites*, exh.cat., London (Tate), 2000, p.169.

4   Robert Hewison, *Ruskin, Turner and the Pre-Raphaelites*, exh.cat., London (Tate), 2000, p.147.

JOHN RUSKIN 1819–1900

Baden, Switzerland

Pencil and watercolour heightened with
white on five sheets of paper, the paper
discoloured, and with further slips making
up the complete format
20⅜ × 15 inches · 517 × 380 mm
(irregularly shaped)
Drawn 1863

COLLECTIONS
Agnew's, London;
Private collection, UK, purchased from the
above 1999, to 2016.

LITERATURE
Eds. E.T. Cook and A. Wedderburn,
The Works of John Ruskin: Library Edition,
London, 1903–12, v.13, p.522;
Paul H. Walton, *Master Drawings by John
Ruskin,* London, 2000, pp.128–133;
Christopher Baker, Ian Jeffrey and Conal
Shields, *John Ruskin: Artist and Observer*,
exh.cat., Edinburgh (National Galleries of
Scotland), 2014, pp.180–181, no.51, repr.

EXHIBITED
London, Royal Society of Painters in Water
Colours, *Ruskin Exhibition*, cat.no.191;
Manchester, Manchester City Art Gallery,
*Catalogue of an Exhibition of Watercolour s and
Drawings by the late John Ruskin*, 1907,
cat.no.126;
Edinburgh, National Galleries of Scotland,
and Ottawa, National Gallery of Canada,
John Ruskin: Artist and Observer, 2014, no.51.

This remarkable drawing was made on the
spot by Ruskin whilst visiting Switzerland
in the summer and autumn of 1863. Ruskin
was consciously following in the footsteps
of Turner and was preparing views of Swiss
towns to be engraved. This vertiginous,
aerial view of Baden is one of the most
ambitious and visually elaborate study
he made whilst on the Continent. The
complex composition was one on which
Ruskin expended a great deal of time and
effort. Writing in his notes on Turner's *The
Harbours of England*, Ruskin observed: 'to
compare my boy's drawing of the Swiss
Baden… made when I was sixteen, with the
hard effort to get it right, in [the present
drawing] – coloured only in a quarter of it
before the autumn leaves fell – then given up
– cut into four – [and] now pasted together
again to show how it was meant to be.'[1]

During the 1850s Ruskin was cataloguing the Turner Bequest. Ruskin became
particularly interested in Turner's late
Swiss watercolours.[2] Ruskin became keen
to retrace Turner's steps and see the towns
Turner had painted. In mid-October 1863
Ruskin returned to northern Switzerland,
basing himself at the Hotel Städthof in
Baden for almost a month, he made frequent
excursions by train to nearby Lauffenburg
and Brugg where, as he reported in a letter,
'I am drawing as hard as I can.'[3] At the same
time he produced a series of important
drawings of Baden itself, the most ambitious
of which was the present work.

In this hugely impressive drawing Ruskin
selected as his view-point a position high
on the bank of the river Limmat, looking
west. The sheets show, on the left hand
side the town's principal Catholic parish
church, while on the right is the Stadtturm

– a defensive tower with distinctive corner turrets that forms the first part of the town's fortifications– which is seen rising up into the distance and following the contour of the hillside above. Ruskin took a position from which to draw the city that allowed a downward view and in which the tiled and dormered roofs form a complex pattern of multi-faceted surfaces. Ruskin preferred these high, almost bird's eye perspectives in his Swiss views. In the distance Ruskin has carefully delineated rust coloured woodland and a meadow, the shadowed surface of which in the lea of the trees has been treated with a vivid touch of blue. In the foreground appears an outcrop of rock, the striations of which point to Ruskin's profound interest in geology.

Ruskin's claim that he made the drawing, cut it up and then reassembled has caused scholars some problems. It has long been asserted that each sheet is from a separate sketchbook page, worked on individually and then assembled and mounted together.[4] Whilst Christopher Newall has suggested that a: 'possible explanation for the curiously composed sheets of paper was that Ruskin began the drawing on a single sheet – probably either that which forms the central right-hand compartment of that at the upper right – and without any clear idea of what the eventual scale and scope might be, but then as his attention wandered more widely across the panorama that lay before him more space was needed that could only be provided by tacking on further sheets.' This seems less likely. Paul Walton has more persuasively offered, that: 'after completing the pencil drawing on a rather large sheet he found it more convenient in his increasingly exposed location to continue with the application of watercolour on smaller pieces of paper. According to a diary entry they were not reassembled until 1873.'[5]

Ruskin had travelled to Switzerland to encounter the landscape of Turner, he had discovered a panoramic breadth which he handled in sheets such as this with a minuteness closer to contemporary Pre-Raphaelite artists. Towns such as Baden also offered a Medieval reality untouched by modernity which appealed to Ruskin's antiquarian instincts. It was a reality under threat, as he wrote to a Swiss friend in 1863: 'I am working [at Baden] and at Lauffenburg with a view to getting some record of these two fine old towns, before they are utterly swept away as others are in Switzerland.'[6] This astounding drawing, in which the colour is well preserved in spite of the staining of the paper, demonstrates Ruskin's dedication and uncompromising approach to recording his world and is undoubtedly one of the masterpieces of Ruskin's time in Switzerland, in its breadth of topography and atmosphere, detail and fluid execution it is a perfect distillation of Ruskin's fascination both with Turner and a newer generation of landscape artists.

J. M. W. Turner
Baden from the South-East, 1844
Pencil, watercolour and pen
9 × 12¾ inches · 228 × 325 mm
Part of the Rheinfelden sketchbook, TB CCCXLIX 14
© Tate, London 2017

NOTES

1   Eds. E.T. Cook and A. Wedderburn, *The Works of John Ruskin: Library Edition*, London, 1903–12, v.13, p.522.
2   Paul H. Walton, *Master Drawings by John Ruskin,* London, 2000, p.128.
3   John Hayman, *John Ruskin and Switzerland*, Ontario, 1990, p.88.
4   Eds. E.T. Cook and A. Wedderburn, *Catalogue of* Drawings, London, 1903–12, cat.no.157.
5   Paul Walton, *Master Drawings by John Ruskin*, London, 2000, pp.130–132.
6   Paul Walton, *Master Drawings by John Ruskin*, London, 2000, p.131.

ALFRED EDWARD CHALON RA 1780–1860

An opera singer

Watercolour on paper
16½ × 12¼ inches · 420 × 310 mm
Painted 1820s.

COLLECTIONS
Edward Croft-Murray (1907–1980);
By descent to 2016.

This impressive depiction of a prima donna taking her curtain call was made by the Swiss born portraitist Alfred Edward Chalon during the 1820s and almost certainly represents one of the leading opera singers of the period. Exquisitely painted in Chalon's refined manner and taken from an unusual view-point – Chalon must have been seated in the front row of the stalls as the footlights frame the bottom of the composition – this portrait is unusual amongst Chalon's portraits of performers as it seems never to have been reproduced as a lithograph.

Alfred Edward Chalon, the son of a watchmaker Jean Chalon, was born at Geneva into a Huguenot family. As a result of the turmoil caused there by the French Revolution, the Chalon family emigrated to England and settled in London, and both Alfred and his older brother, the landscape and genre painter John James Chalon trained as artists at the Royal Academy Schools. Alfred first exhibited there in 1810, was elected an ARA two years later and RA in 1816. Throughout the 1820s Chalon produced a number of portraits of famous performers, particularly opera singers. Chalon's portrait of *Giuditta Pasta* in the role of Queen Semiramide from Rossini's opera of the same name was painted in 1828. Chalon exhibited a portrait of another singer in a Rossini opera at the Royal Academy in 1823: *Madame Ronzi de Begnis in the character of*

Fatima in the opera of 'Pietro l'Ermita', now in the National Portrait Gallery, London. In 1829 Chalon exhibited at the Royal Academy a portrait of the great German operatic soprano, Henriette Sontag, Countess Rossi. Along with these exhibition works, Chalon produced a number of more informal caricatures of famous singers, including Maria Dickons and Angelica Catalani.

Catalani is a possible candidate for the present portrait; her strong, dark features are certainly consistent with existing likenesses of Catalani. Frustratingly this is one of the very few theatrical portraits by Chalon which he did not have reproduced as a lithograph by Richard James Lane. Despite the anonymity of the sitter, the portrait is one of the most dramatic and impressive of Chalon's theatrical subjects underlining the celebrity of operatic sopranos in London during the 1820s.

Robert Dighton
Madame Catalani in Semiramide, 1806
Hand-coloured etching
11⅛ × 8 inches · 282 × 205 mm
© The Trustees of the British Museum

Warrant appointing Alfred Edward Chalon 'Portrait painter in watercolour' to Queen Victoria, 9 August 1837
Collection of Lowell Libson Ltd.

Alfred Edward Chalon *Self-portrait*
Black and red chalk, touched with grey ink and white
9¾ × 6¾ inches · 249 × 172 mm
Signed and dated 1847
© The Trustees of the British Museum

ALFRED EDWARD CHALON RA 1780–1860

Giuditta Pasta as Semiramide

Watercolour on two sheets of paper
16½ × 12¼ inches · 420 × 310 mm
Inscribed and dated lower left:
Semiramide 1828

COLLECTIONS
Edward Croft-Murray (1907–1980);
By descent to 2016.

ENGRAVED
by Richard James Lane, lithograph,
published July 1837 by J. Mitchell.

This dramatic portrait of the great Italian
soprano, Giuditta Pasta (1797–1867), in the
role of Queen Semiramide from Rossini's
opera of the same name, is part of a series
of studies made by Alfred Edward Chalon
of theatrical performances during the 1820s.
Giuditta Pasta was acknowledged as one

Richard James Lane, after A. E. Chalon
Giuditta Pasta as Semiramide
Lithograph with hand-colouring on chine collé
20¾ × 15⅛ inches · 526 × 383 mm
Published July 1837 by J. Mitchell, London
© The Trustees of the British Museum

of the most prominent singers of the 1820s
famed not only for her extraordinary if
flawed voice, but also for the physicality of
her performances. As Susan Rutherford has
noted: 'her innovative practices contributed
to the development and reconceptualization
of opera's dramatic potential on the
Romantic stage.' Pasta made her reputation
in a series of dramatic roles, including as
Norma from Bellini's opera of the same
name, Amina in Bellini's *La Sonnambula*
and as Donizetti's Anna Bolena, but her
most famous role, as seen here, was as
Queen Semiramide.

Chalon became famous for his flattering
depictions of his female sitters and was closely associated with the London stage, making
numerous portrait studies of the leading
dancers and opera singers of the period.
Many of these works were reproduced by
leading lithographers, often in colour. A set
of six Chalon sketches of Taglioni in various
roles, lithographed by R. J. Lee, and with
poems by W. N. Bayley, was published in 1831.
It was perhaps natural that Chalon would
depict Giuditta Pasta.

The present portrait depicts Pasta in her
iconic role, as the fated Babylonian Queen
Semiramide, from Rossini's 1823 opera of the
same name. The dramatic pose was characteristic of Pasta's physicality and stage presence. She was described in 1829 by the critic
Carlo Ritorni as the 'cantante delle passioni',
noting that her voice was directed: 'towards
expressing the most intense passions, accompanying it with expressions of physical action,
unknown before her in the lyric theatre.'[1]

Chalon's drawing is inscribed 'Semiramide'
and dated 1828; it is therefore not a depiction
of the opera's London premier in 1824, but its
revival at the King's Theatre four years later.

The London Magazine noted 'The theatre
has … been crammed, for all persons who
pretend to good taste, or who know how to
admire exquisite singing and finished acting
go to see Madame Pasta.' *The Times* reported
the first night of the run, noting:
*Madame Pastas, as the Babylonian Queen, was
on Saturday as powerfully effective as on all
former occasions. Such is the peculiar influence
exercised by her intense conception of great
characters, that her latest efforts always increase
the previous impression made on her audience.
The universal applause of an excessively crowded
house, which marked her reception when she
first came on the stage, was partly meant,
perhaps to show all that was expected of her;
and the enthusiastic manner in which approbation was testified at the different periods of her
performance, must have convinced her that the
expectations she had raised were realized in a
manner which fully justified them.*[2]

Pasta's fame meant that Chalon's
watercolour would inevitably find a popular
audience and Richard Lane produced a
lithograph of the drawing in the 1830s.

Showing Pasta in the roll of the
murderous Queen, Chalon's energetic
watercolour perfectly communicates the
singer's physicality and the drama of
Rossini's opera. As a popular, contemporary
depiction of one of the greatest sopranos of
the nineteenth-century en role in one of the
most demanding rolls in the repertoire, this
drawing is of exceptional importance.

NOTES
1 Susan Rutherford, 'La Contante delle
passioni': Giuditta Pasta and the Idea of
Operatic Performance', *Cambridge Opera
Journal*, v.19, n.2, July 2007, pp.109.
2 *The Times*, Monday 21 April 1828.

Semiramide 1823

ALFRED EDWARD CHALON RA 1780–1860

Madame Céleste Elliott in Bayle Bernard's 'St Mary's Eve'

Watercolour on paper
14½ × 10½ inches · 370 × 270 mm,
the top corners cropped, as lithographed
Signed and dated, lower left: *A E Chalon RA*
& C 1838

COLLECTIONS
Edward Croft-Murray (1907–1980);
By descent to 2016.

ENGRAVED
by Maxim Gauci, *Madame Céleste as Madeline in*
St Mary's Eve, lithograph, published June 1838
by Hodgson & Graves, London.

This extraordinary portrait shows one of the
most celebrated dancers of the nineteenth-
century, Céleste Elliott, known as Madame
Céleste, in a role from the American play-
wright William Bayle Bernard's *St Mary's Eve:*
A Solway Story. Madame Céleste had a highly
successful career as a dancer and melodramat-
ic performer in both Britain and the United
States; her fame in the US was only matched
by that of Fanny Kemble and Jenny Lind. This
beautifully observed, dynamic portrait was
part of a sequence of images Alfred Edward
Chalon made of famous performers in
London during the 1820s and 1830s; as a major
international celebrity on both sides of the
Atlantic, Madame Céleste's image was widely
known and the present drawing was published
as a popular lithograph in 1838.

Born Céleste Céline in Paris, probably in
around 1810, she was enrolled as a pupil of the
Paris conservatory where she performed with
François-Joseph Talma and Madame Pasta.
Her first professional appearance was in 1827 at
the Bowery Theatre in New York, in which she
danced a *pas seul* with a Parisian dance troupe.
During her visit to the United States, Céleste
also performed in small ballets in theatres
on the east coast. In 1828 she married Henry

Elliott of Baltimore, with whom she had
a daughter, born in 1829. Elliott died soon
after their marriage. In 1830 Madame Céleste
arrived in Liverpool from New Orleans,
and made her début in England as Fenella,
the wronged mute sister of the Neapolitan
fisherman hero, Masaniello, in Auber's opera
of that name. Mute parts enabled Céleste to
display her brilliant skills as a versatile and
expressive mime artist, and also conveniently
concealed her always halting command of
the English language.

In her second tour to the United States,
from 1834 to 1837, she became a theatrical
sensation and box-office star. In America she
became famous for her pantomimic roles
in plays such as *The Wizard Skiff, or, The*
Tongueless Pirate Boy, *The Wept of the Wish-*
Ton-Wish (adapted from Fenimore Cooper's
novel), and *The Dumb Brigand* as well as for
her prowess as a dancer in the ballet of *La*
Bayadère. Writing after her death, in 1882, the
Gentleman's Magazine noted:
It would be a difficult matter at the present
juncture to realise the enthusiasm which
Celeste's acting evoked in those early days
throughout the New World. No other actress
was ever more popularly hailed there, and the
memory of none ever remained so long green in
the hearts of the American people. Cheered to
the echo of the soldiery, affectionately greeted
by the populace, and unanimously elected a
Free Citizen of the States, her cup of joy was
surely full to overflowing. In Kentucky not a
seat remained untaken for several weeks before
her advertised appearance. Moreover, when she
reached Washington, General Jackson politely
insisted upon introducing her to the members of
the Cabinet, that she might receive the congratu-
lations due to one who had been so recently
honoured with the freedom of the States.

Maxim Gauci, after Alfred Edward Chalon
Madame Céleste as Madeline in St Mary's Eve
Lithograph, published June 1838,
21⅝ × 14⅞ inches · 550 × 378 mm
© The Trustees of the British Museum

A. E. Chalon. R.A. &c. 1838.

DUDLEY HARDY 1865–1922

Sarah Bernhardt

Oil on panel
12 × 9⅝ inches · 305 × 245 mm
Signed lower left
Painted *c.*1890

COLLECTIONS
Private collection, France, to 2010;
Lowell Libson Ltd;
Private collection, UK,
purchased from the above 2011,
to 2016.

This unusual portrait depicts Sarah Bernhardt, the most famous actress of the late nineteenth century. Painted by the painter and illustrator Dudley Hardy, the portrait is one of several he completed of Bernhardt and shows her seated in profile, wearing a pink fur-trimmed robe and holding a quill pen from which ink is dripping. A document with a red wax seal is beside her and candle burns on the table next to the pot of ink. The pen possibly alludes to her literary aspirations; after her first attempt at writing in 1878, *In the Clouds, Impressions of a chair*, following a flight in a hot air balloon; Bernhardt went on to produce a drama in one act and prose *The Confession* in 1886. Although it as it appears to be a legal document, the painting make in fact commemorate perhaps Bernhardt's management of the *Théâtre de la Renaissance*. Hardy's technique and vigorous brushwork give the picture an animated sense of urgency quite unlike his smaller study of the actress painted in 1889 (Sterling and Francine Clark Art Institute, Williamstown).

Dudley Hardy was the son of the marine painter T. B. Hardy, he trained with his father in England and later at the Academy in Düsseldorf, followed by study in Antwerp and Paris, before returning to London, where he exhibited at the Royal Academy from 1884 until his death in 1922. While Hardy was best known as an illustrator and cartoonist, he also painted landscapes, seascapes, oriental, biblical and genre subjects and designed theatre posters. His Royal Society of British Artists exhibit of 1893 showed his social conscience, *Sans Asile* (1888) depicting huddled homeless figures sleeping in Trafalgar Square. The

Dudley Hardy
Sarah Bernhardt, 1889
Oil on panel · 9½ × 6⁹⁄₁₆ inches · 241 × 166 mm
© Sterling and Francine Clark Art Institute, Williamstown, Massachusetts, USA

Jules Bastien-Lepage
Sarah Bernhardt, 1879,
Colour lithograph, from the oil portrait in a private collection, USA.

Dudley Hardy
A Gaiety Girl, 1893
Colour lithograph poster
Private collection/Bridgeman Images

painting was subsequently exhibited on the Continent, and established his reputation.

Hardy made his the field of graphic art – his talents in this area coinciding with the increase in illustrated magazine publication and poster production at the turn of the century. The influence of French graphic style is seen in his fluent line and use of tone. Hardy's *Gaiety Girl* poster series of the 1890s show the influence of Jules Chéret, however he developed his own characteristically English approach with his simplified style and integrated lettering. Hardy's most famous image was the *Yellow Girl* which he created to advertise the magazine *To-Day*. He designed several posters for the Savoy Theatre, including those for the D'Oyly Carte operas. Hardy was in Paris from 1888 to 1890 and it was during this time he met Sarah Bernhardt, then at the height of her fame.

Bernhardt was born in Paris in 1844 the first of the three daughters of Julie Bernhardt, a Jewish courtesan from Amsterdam. The identity of her father remains unknown. She made her debut at the *Theatre Française* (later the Comedie Française) in 1862 in Racine's *Iphigenie en Aulide*, which was only a moderate success and she soon left the company after a clash of personalities. Bernhardt returned to the *Comedie Française* in 1872 and went on to consolidate her position, which by the time the company appeared in London in 1879, was as the undoubted star of the French stage. After a hugely successful season in London in 1880, Bernhardt broke away from the security of the *Comedie Française* and embarked upon an independent career with the first of six tours of America.

Bernhardt had a large circle of artistic friends in Paris and was the subject of numerous portraits, by amongst others Louise Abbéma, Georges Clairin and Jules Bastien-Lepage. Hardy painted Bernhardt on at least two occasions and in both portraits he emphasised Bernhardt's slender form, erect posture and mountain of auburn hair. The present painting combines Hardy's graphic line with a painterly energy – Hardy has executed some passages of painting with his fingers – to present a highly individual depictions of one of the icons of the nineteenth century stage.

HENRY MOORE 1898–1986
Figure studies

Chalk, ink and wash on prepared paper
14¾ × 21½ inches · 375 × 547 mm
Signed and dated, lower right: *Moore 33.*

COLLECTIONS
Francis Parker Kinnicutt (1908–1961);
Mr and Mrs James R. Houghton,
daughter and son-in-law of the above, 2016.

LITERATURE
Ann Garrould ed., *Henry Moore,
Complete Drawings* 1984–86, Addenda and
Index 1916–86, vol.7, London, p.14,
HMF 1014a, p.15, repr.

This bold drawing was made by Henry
Moore at a key moment in his pre-war
career, as he was establishing himself as
Britain's leading sculptor and a major artist
with an international reputation. Signed
and dated 1933, the drawing was executed
the year Moore joined Unit One, a group
of leading modernist painters, sculptors
and architects led by Paul Nash. Through
its group exhibitions and publication, the
movement attempted to reconcile abstraction and surrealism, the two principal
currents in British art. Moore's fluid, ink
drawing demonstrates how receptive he was
to the currents of Surrealism at the same
time pointing to his organic approach to the
human form in his sculpture.

The 1930s represent the most innovative
and original years of Henry Moore's career.
They also saw a proliferation of exhibitions
at home, and Moore's work was included
for the first time in exhibitions abroad. In

1930 Moore, with Jacob Epstein and John
Skeaping, was invited to represent British
sculpture at the Venice Biennale. In the
following year Moore exhibited three works
at an international sculpture exhibition at
the Kunsthaus, Zürich. It was also in 1931
that the Museum für Kunst und Gewerbe,
Hamburg, made the first purchase by a
museum of a Moore sculpture. In April 1931
Moore held his second one-man exhibition
in London, at the Leicester Galleries. In
his brief foreword to the catalogue, Jacob
Epstein wrote: 'Before these works I ponder
in silence ... For the future of sculpture in
England, Henry Moore is vitally important.'[1]

In 1931 Moore joined the Seven and Five
Society possibly as a result of the summer
holiday which he had spent in 1931 at
Happisburgh on the Norfolk coast with Ivon
Hitchens and Ben Nicholson, who were
already members. He exhibited with the
group in the following year, and again in 1935

Henry Moore
Reclining figure: drawing for sculpture, 1933
Pen and ink, brush and ink, wash
14⅜ × 15 inches · 364 × 380 mm
Art Gallery of New South Wales
Reproduced by permission of the Henry Moore
Foundation (HMF992)

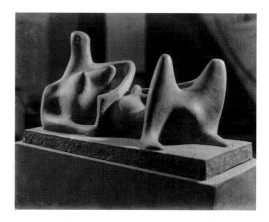

Henry Moore
Reclining Figure, 1933
Reinforced carved concrete
20¾ × 31½ × 12½ inches · 527 × 800 × 318 mm
Mildred Lane Kemper Art Museum, Washington University
Reproduced by permission of the Henry Moore Foundation
(LH134)

at the society's last show. The Seven and Five Society exhibitions were the principal forum for abstraction in London, but Moore never abandoned the human form. By contrast, throughout the 1930s Moore was hugely influenced by the work of Picasso and surrealist sculpture of Jean Arp and Alberto Giacometti; their work liberated Moore's imagination in the direction of more elusive, more evocative, organic forms.

This drawing neatly encapsulates these diverse influences. The central forms, particularly the figure in the left foreground and the heavily worked reclining figure on the right suggest the impact of Picasso, particularly the sculptural drawings Picasso made in the late 1920s. The ghostly, wash figures that populate the background of the composition all point to Moore's interest in surrealism. Whilst Moore's work as a draughtsman was distinct from his practice as a sculptor, there was a dialogue between the two mediums. The reclining female figure was the central motif of Moore's sculpture and it is notable that in this drawing it has received the most sustained working. Moore produced several sculptures in 1933 which explored the same form; for example his carved concrete *Reclining Figure* now in the Mildred Lane Kemper Art Museum in St Louis.

The birth of Unit One was announced by Paul Nash in a letter to *The Times* in June 1933, although the group's first exhibition, at the Mayor Gallery, Cork Street, London, was not held until April 1934. The show coincided with the publication of *Unit One: the Modern Movement in English Architecture, Painting and Sculpture*, edited by Herbert Read, to which each of the eleven members contributed a statement. Moore and Hepworth were the two sculptors in the group. In Moore's statement, his most expansive airing to date of his views on the art of sculpture, he discussed five qualities in sculpture which had become of fundamental importance to him: truth to material, full three-dimensional realization, observation of natural objects, vision and expression, and vitality and power of expression. Herbert Read's *Henry Moore, Sculptor: an Appreciation*, the first monograph on the artist, was published the following year. Read was unreserved in his praise of Moore's achievement stating that: 'in the fullness of his powers, he offers us the perfected product of his genius.'[2]

Preserved in excellent condition, Moore's *Figure Studies* demonstrates the breadth and intelligence of his work as a sculptor, giving the graphic context for his sculptural work. Part of a group of drawings Moore made at this crucial moment, when he was reaching real celebrity as a sculptor and part of a series of important British modernist movements, the drawing distils the diverse and international influences which were driving his highly original work.

NOTES

1 Quoted in Roger Berthoud, *The Life of Henry Moore*, London, 2003, p.115.
2 Quoted in Roger Berthoud, *The Life of Henry Moore*, London, 2003, p.136.

LOWELL
LIBSON LTD
BRITISH ART

We have an international reputation as the specialist dealers in British art with an emphasis on paintings, watercolours, drawings and sculpture of the seventeenth- to mid-nineteenth centuries. Lowell Libson Ltd is recognised for handling works of outstanding quality backed with exceptional scholarship and as a result we count many leading American, European and British museums and private collectors amongst our regular clients. The gallery exhibits at TEFAF MAASTRICHT and TEFAF NEW YORK FALL, as well as during LONDON ART WEEK. We produce a full scholarly catalogue of recently acquired highlights from our inventory annually, which can be downloaded from our website.

We believe passionately in advancing scholarship in British art and actively support art historical research in both Britain and America. The gallery has sponsored a number of important exhibitions in recent years including: *Thomas Gainsborough's Landscapes* at the Holburne Museum, Bath, 2011; *Constable, Gainsborough, Turner and the Making of Landscape* at the Royal Academy, 2012; *Joseph Wright of Derby: Bath and Beyond* at the Holburne Museum, Bath, 2014; *Great British Drawings* at the Ashmolean, Oxford, 2015 and *Jonathan Richardson By Himself* at The Courtauld Gallery, 2015. We have also mounted several significant loan exhibitions in Clifford Street including *Masterpieces of English Watercolours and Drawings from the National Gallery of Scotland* and of works by Thomas Rowlandson drawn from British private collections.

We believe that the process of acquiring a work of art should be an enjoyable and stimulating experience and pride themselves on having created a gallery that offers clients the opportunity to discuss and view pictures in discreet and comfortable surroundings. We have a carefully selected stock of the highest quality and interest within a wide price range and we act as both principals and agents in the purchase and sale of works of art giving clients great flexibility and choice. We are able to offer advice on all aspects of collecting pictures. This includes the purchase and sale of works of art as well as conservation, restoration, framing, lighting and hanging. We can also provide a complete curatorial service for collections.

Visitors are always welcome at the gallery which is located on the second floor of an attractive building dating from the 1880s situated between New Bond Street and Savile Row. Although we are generally open on weekdays we operate on a 'by appointment' basis, to ensure that we can give our visitors our best attention.

www.lowell-libson.com

LOWELL LIBSON LTD
BRITISH ART

3 CLIFFORD STREET · LONDON W1S 2LF

Telephone: +44 (0)20 7734 8686
Email: pictures@lowell-libson.com
Website: www.lowell-libson.com

The gallery is open by appointment, Monday to Friday
The entrance is in Old Burlington Street

Published by Lowell Libson Limited 2017
Text and publication © Lowell Libson Limited
All rights reserved

ISBN 978 0 9929096 2 8

Designed and typeset in Dante by Dalrymple
Photography by Rodney Todd-White & Son Ltd
Colour reproduction by Altaimage Ltd
Printed in Belgium by Albe De Coker

Cover: a sheet of 18th-century Italian paste paper
(collection: Lowell Libson)

Inside covers: Henry Moore
details from *Figure studies*, see page 114

Frontispiece: John Hamilton Mortimer
detail from *Self-portrait*, see page 22

Page 7, opposite introduction: John Ruskin
detail from *Bellinzona*, see page 98